Late Gothic Art from Cologne

ERRATUM

As this catalogue went to press, four of the objects intended for the exhibition were unable to travel.

They are nos.18, 31 and one object from nos.12 and 15 respectively.

The National Gallery

Late Gothic Art from Cologne

A loan exhibition

5th April to 1st June 1977

Published by Order of the Trustees, Publications Department
National Gallery, London

Catalogue designed by James Shurmer

Set in Monotype Bembo and
printed by T & A Constable Ltd
Edinburgh

Cover:
The Coronation of the Virgin (details),
by the Master of Saint Lawrence
(cat.no.8)

Frontispiece:
Saints Alexius and Agnes (detail),
by the Master of
the Saint Bartholomew Altarpiece
(cat.no.37)

Foreword

German art of every period–including that of the 20th century–has remained probably the most undervalued of all the European schools by the public in England. That is both sad and silly. It is always sad when great art of any kind is neglected, and it is silly to let prejudice or ill-based assumptions prevent one from enjoying a fresh aesthetic experience.

In welcoming this loan exhibition from the museums of Cologne to the National Gallery, we do so on two counts: first, of course, for its own sake as a revelation of the high and exquisite artistic achievements of a famous city in the 15th century, but secondly as an encouragement to deeper awareness and exploration of German art altogether. An encounter with the Gothic grace, refinement, and recherché colour of the Cologne School painters, headed by Stephan Lochner, is perhaps as good an encouragement as any to explore further the rich, accomplished, often fantastic world of art in Germany.

A loan exhibition comparable to the present one has never before been made to England. We are profoundly grateful to the Cologne museum authorities who have generously agreed to it, chosen it and catalogued it. Our chief debt of gratitude must be to Dr. Gerhard Bott, Generaldirektor of the Cologne Museums, who initiated it and has enthusiastically supported it throughout in every way. We are also grateful to Dr. Anton Legner, of the Schnütgen Museum, for his enthusiasm and valuable support and to Dr. Hugo Stehkämper for his willingness to lend three extremely fine manuscripts from the Historisches Archiv der Stadt Köln.

The opportunity has been taken to supplement these loans with pictures by some of the Cologne painters in the National Gallery. In addition, some relevant pictures from English collections have been borrowed. The Victoria & Albert Museum has once again generously lent to us, and we are grateful for loans from the Courtauld Institute of Art and the National Trust. We are also much indebted to the Earl of Halifax and to two other private owners, who wish to remain anonymous, for allowing us to borrow pictures.

The organisation of the exhibition in London has been the responsibility of Alistair Smith, Deputy Keeper in charge of the German pictures at the Gallery. He has also been responsible for its mounting and for editing and supplementing the catalogue. The design of the exhibition has been carried out by Richard Mosedale of the Department of the Environment, to whom we are indebted.

Major exhibitions of this kind place a considerable burden on many members of the National Gallery staff, and I am grateful to them all for responding yet once more to extra tasks. Much is owed to Alistair Smith for his profound involvement with the exhibition from its first conception to the accomplished fact; his scholarly appreciation of the period is accompanied by a wish to share that appreciation with as wide a public as possible – and that is exactly what this exhibition aims to do.

Michael Levey, Director

Contents

Translation from the German
by Heidi Grieve and (in small part) Alistair Smith

Date chart of the artists

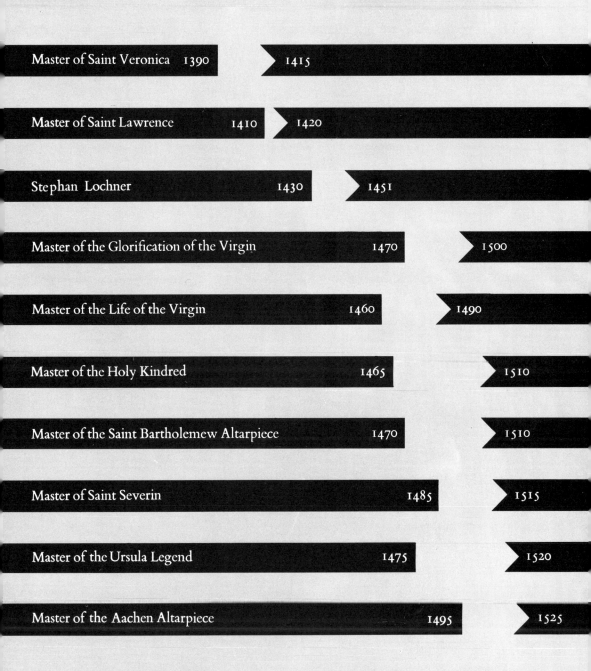

The chart displays
the approximate span of activity
of each artist

Master of Saint Veronica   1390   1415

Master of Saint Lawrence   1410   1420

Stephan Lochner   1430   1451

Master of the Glorification of the Virgin   1470   1500

Master of the Life of the Virgin   1460   1490

Master of the Holy Kindred   1465   1510

Master of the Saint Bartholemew Altarpiece   1470   1510

Master of Saint Severin   1485   1515

Master of the Ursula Legend   1475   1520

Master of the Aachen Altarpiece   1495   1525

Paintings
and Illuminated
Manuscripts

It is small wonder that the study of medieval painting, which began in the early 19th century, started with the Cologne school. The Romantics found in Cologne Cathedral a symbol of medieval Germany, and paintings from the town became the focal point of their researches. Schlegel was the first to use the term 'Cologne School' in 1805, and to recognise in it 'an individual, independent style'. It soon came to be recognised that, around 1400, Cologne was one of the most important centres of art production, the equal of Paris, Dijon and Vienna.

Medieval Cologne provided ideal circumstances for a broad expansion of art. The town was well endowed. A rich aristocracy and a self-conscious middle class provided, together with the numerous churches and other religious foundations as well as the archbishopric itself, a great impetus of patronage. In addition, there was a considerable demand for art from outside the town itself, partly because of the concentration of the transport industry upon Cologne, and partly because of the city's widespread trade links.

Cologne, in the Middle Ages, had 40,000 inhabitants, and was thus the most densely populated town in Germany. In size, it was the largest in Europe, being protected by a wall which was a hardly credible eight kilometres long. The wealth of the town, always visible in the permanent buzz of building activity, was founded on the so-called *Stapelrecht* ('staple-law') which Archbishop Konrad von Hochstaden granted the town in 1349. This law stated that all wares passing through Cologne (which occupied a crucial position on important trading routes) had to be stored, examined and taxed there. In consequence, the inhabitants of Cologne were assured of a dominant role as merchants, which they asserted throughout their membership of the Hanseatic league. The city was one of the most powerful towns of the league; it was to it that delegates of the league were called in 1367; and it was there that there was established the 'Cologne Confederation' (a protective agreement between the numerous towns of the Hansa).

At an early date the people of Cologne attempted to take their fate into their own hands, and to defend themselves against the inherited territorial powers and privileges of the aristocracy. In 1288, after the battle of Worringen, the archbishops were forced to reside outside the town boundary; after an abortive attempt by the weavers (1370) to relieve the patricians of power, the guilds succeeded, in 1396, in taking over the government of the town. In the *Verbundbrief* ('letter of confederation') they laid down a 'democratic' constitution by which, from that time on, the guilds elected the majority of the 49 council members (see cat.no.41). The wonderful tower of the Ratshaus, built between 1407 and 1414 with the confiscated wealth of the patricians, was a symbol of the new self-consciousness and self-definition. Finally, in 1475 the German Emperor granted Cologne the privileges of a '*Freie Reichstadt*' (a self-governing town of the Empire).

The very number of extant paintings of the Cologne school is proof that the town provided a good base for the art industry. About 350 pictures are known to us from the period up to 1500. (If one compares this number with those from other artistic towns or regions, this number is very high, and yet this may represent only 2 or 3 per cent of the original total.)

In regard to the paintings themselves, research is faced with many problems. Many different workshops and groups of artists existed. Yet although the documents are full of artists' names, and although some exact information is known about one or two of them, it has been found impossible to bring documentary evidence and extant works into correlation. The one exception is the *Dombild* ('cathedral painting'), which is identified as by Stephan Lochner through an entry in Albrecht Dürer's Netherlandish diary. The majority of Cologne painters remain anonymous; their creations being tradesman's work, which was not signed.

Art historians have, therefore, been forced to invent 'nicknames' and to construct fictive personalities around the qualities which they discern in the major works. Under the name of the Master of Such-and-such (e.g. the 'Master of the Saint Bartholomew Altarpiece') are classified a number of works with certain qualities in common. In addition, few works are dated, either by inscription or by document. Thus the art historian is thrown back on stylistic comparison, scientific methods of dating the materials used, and a systematic examination of the sources.

The most noticeable characteristic of the school is the high quality of craftsmanship. The guild laid down regulations about the quality of materials to be used; and in addition imposed strict tests on those who wished to be admitted to the guild. Article 8 of the regulations read 'No man from outside Cologne can enter this guild without giving proof of his abilities, and without first paying his membership fee.'

The strict management of the guild was perhaps partially responsible for the strong element of tradition in Cologne painting. This manifests itself in several ways: the use of the same subject-matter throughout the whole century; the preservation of gold and brocade backgrounds; saints set out in simple rows; compositions adhering to a strict symmetry. Only gradually were innovations in the depiction of space and perspective accepted; realism fought a bitter struggle with a strong preference for the preservation and even re-introduction of *retardataire* elements. This can be seen in the types of picture themselves: the devotional image played a most important role, as did also the triptych and diptych. Complicated altar-forms, like the polyptych, are seldom seen.

Cologne painting was *Gothic*—conservative and non-revolutionary. Nevertheless, through travel and the movement of pictures themselves, the Cologne painter became aware of the new art. This influx from the West marked many Cologne works. There is recognisable in the paintings on the cupboards of the cathedral choir (1325–35) both French and English influence; examples of book-painting (see no.40) show English characteristics, while '*The Small Calvary*' (see no.7) is close to French painting. This foreign influence came to Cologne and was subsumed in the local style. The generation between Lochner (d.1451) and the Master of Saint Severin (about 1500) orientated themselves increasingly to this art from the West. Art works too like the Wasservass-Altar and the famous altar by Rogier van der Weyden, which was in the church of Saint Columba, were points of comparison and influence for the Cologne workshops.

The stylistic development of panel- and book-painting in Cologne shows a constant relationship between foreign and native art. In the few remaining examples from around 1400 there is displayed a new joy in narrative and a closer relationship with realism. Although, in the early 14th century, book painting clearly provided the models for the panel-painter, now panels began to play the leading role. This was the time of the 'soft' or International Gothic style, and Cologne painters stood then at the head of the artistic *avant-garde*. They did not *develop* the new style at all, but rather took it over and extracted the maximum from its possibilities. This put in motion the springtime of Cologne painting —the leading masters included the Masters of Saint Veronica and of St. Lawrence (nos.6–10). Painting changed from a jagged style to a soft, more painterly method, in which the devotional image became a central point. Among many considerable examples, there originated here some creations of European importance, like the *St. Veronica with the Sudarium* (Munich) or '*The Small Calvary*' (see nos.6 and 7).

The generation of these painters came to an end about 1440, about the time that Lochner began to develop. This highly gifted painter came from outside Cologne, brought to it a fresh knowledge of the newest art, and became the most important painter for succeeding generations. Reminiscences of his style, his compositions and his subject-matter are still perceptible in the work of the generation around 1500.

One of the principal heirs to his art was the Master of the Glorification of the Virgin (nos.17,18). His art features many quotations from Lochner.

Cologne painting of the second half of the 15th century is seen to develop an increasing acceptance of reality, sometimes manifesting itself in attention to detail, at others demonstrating a concern for space, or for realism in figures or in landscape. It seems that the Cologne painters of this generation orientated themselves mainly towards Rogier van der Weyden and to Dieric Bouts, all of them trying in their different ways to absorb their influence. Of these, the Master of the Life of the Virgin, and his collaborator the Master of the Lyversberg Passion, concerned themselves principally with the relationship between space and figure, the Master of the Holy Kindred with realism of detail and with a new comprehension of monumental composition. The Master of the Saint Bartholomew Altarpiece concentrated on the plasticity of the body and on the spatial dimension while the Master of Saint Severin founded a more intimate vocabulary and a free, painterly form. The last phase of late Gothic painting in Cologne gives, once more, the picture of a sharp contrast with the latest developments of Western European painting.

Frank Günter Zehnder

Cologne Exhib., 1961. Der Meister des Bartholomäus-Altares, der Meister des Aachener Altares. Kölner Maler der Spätgotik. Ausstellung im Wallraf-Richartz-Museum zu Köln 1961.

Cologne Exhib., 1970. Herbst des Mittelalters. Spätgotik in Köln und am Niederrhein. Kunsthalle Köln 1970.

Cologne Exhib., 1974. Von Stefan Lochner. Die Kölner Maler von 1300 bis 1430. Wallraf-Richartz-Museum Köln 1974.

Goldberg and Scheffler. Gisela Goldberg und Gisela Scheffler, Bayerische Staatsgemäldesammlungen, Alte Pinakothek München. Gemäldekataloge. Band XIV. Altdeutsche Gemälde, Köln und Nordwestdeutschland. München 1972.

A. Legner, 1970. Anton Legner, Spätgotische Skulpturen im Schnütgen-Museum. Cologne 1970.

Levey. Michael Levey, National Gallery Catalogues. The German School. London 1959.

Manchester Exhib., 1961. German Art (1400–1800) from Collections in Great Britain. City Art Gallery, Manchester 1961.

Das Schnutgen-Museum. Das Schnütgen-Museum 4. Aufl. Köln 1968.

Stange. Alfred Stange. Kritisches Verzeichnis der deutschen Tafelbilder vor Dürer. Band I. München 1967.

Zehnder, 1973. F. G. Zehnder, Der Meister der hl. Veronika, Dissertation Bonn, 1973.

(Right) '*The Small Calvary*', by the Master of Saint Veronica (cat.no.7)

Cologne Master of around 1400

1. Crucifixion with the Virgin, St. John and a Donor

The Virgin stands to the left of the cross, praying and mourning; to the right of the cross St. John, carrying a book, turns and points to the cross with his left hand. The donor, in clerical dress, kneels at the foot of the cross on stony, almost barren, ground. Above his head is a scroll. The gilt background is of repoussé work; in it two angels can be seen at either side of Christ's head.

The little panel is still in its original frame. Connected with the Two Kings (see no.2), it formed the front of the right wing of a small triptych, whose centre panel is lost, presumably split up at the beginning of the 19th century. The corresponding left wing is in the Alte Pinakothek in Munich and shows on its inner side the *Annunciation*, on its outer side the left half of the *Adoration of the Kings* (see no.2). The Munich panel has also been split.

The triptych was almost certainly used for private devotion; its donor was a canon. This type of Crucifixion, with Christ's body stretched and slightly arched, was widely used in Cologne painting from the end of the 14th century onwards and found its most sensitive formulation in the works of the Master of St. Veronica.

Oak, 31 × 18cm (1ft ¼in × 7in) (painted surface); 33·5 × 20·7cm (1ft 1¼ × 8⅛in) (panel size). The lettering in the scroll above the donor has been rubbed off. Restored in 1950.
From the Wallraf Collection.
Literature: E. Buchner, *Malerei der deutschen Spätgotik*, München 1960, p.8; Stange, no.25; G. Goldberg and G. Scheffler, p.124ff.
Cologne, Wallraf-Richartz Museum, no.WRM334.

**Cologne Master of
around 1400**

2. Two Holy Kings

The two kings stand in a meadow full of flowers. The king on the left turns and points with his right hand towards the star, in his left he carries his gift, a precious vessel. The second king who, like the first, is dressed in splendid clothes and wears a crown holds a similar vessel in both hands. His stance and the gesture of the left king suggest that they move from right to left. The dark background is ornamented with a repeat pattern of gilt columbines.

The picture is still in its original frame and depressions on the right still indicate where the hinges were. The panel was originally the back of the *Crucifixion* panel (see no.1). Together they made up the right wing of a triptych. Its centre panel is lost, but the left wing is in the *Alte Pinakothek* in Munich. On the inner side it shows the Annunciation, on the outer side the Virgin and Child and Joseph in a stable with one king adoring the Child. (Not included in the Exhibition but illustrated opposite.) The two panels were probably split in the early 19th century. When the wings were closed (Cologne and Munich panels) the complete scene of the *Adoration of the Kings* could originally be seen. While the interior of the triptych showed scenes from the lives of Christ and the Virgin, the exterior presented a typical Cologne subject (see Index of Saints: Three Magi). It is possible that the donor, who wears the robes of a canon (see no.1), was a member of the Chapter of Cologne Cathedral.

Oak, 30·5 × 18cm (1ft × 7in) (painted surface), 33·5 × 20·3 (1ft 1¼in × 8in) (panel size).
From the Wallraf Collection, Cologne.
Literature: Stange, no.25; Goldberg and Scheffler, pp.124ff.
Cologne, Wallraf-Richartz Museum, no.WRM335.

20

3. The Adoration of
the Three Kings

Behind the Virgin and Child stands Joseph. In the top left-hand corner, on the roof of the hut, an angel holds a scroll. The gilt background of the picture is of repoussé work.

The panel is still in its original frame. For the subject see Index of Saints: Three Magi. The painter of this panel records the story in a simple manner. The figures are pushed close together and the human interest outweighs the representation of majesty.

The panel was formerly attributed to the Cologne School, then to the School of the Lower Rhine. Stange thought he could detect a direct Bohemian influence; but the style and structuring of the panel rather suggest that it originated in central Germany.

Oak, 55 × 38cm (1ft 9½in × 1ft 1in) (painted surface), 57·8 × 40·7cm (1ft 10¾in × 1ft 4in) (panel size). On the angel's scroll: *gloria in excelsi*. Restored in 1941.
From the Wallraf Collection, Cologne.
Literature: L. Küppers, *Die Heiligen Drei Könige*, Recklinghausen 1964, pp.17,31f;
J. Hiller-H. Vey, *Katalog der deutschen und niederländischen Gemälde bis 1550 im Wallraf-Richartz-Museum und im Kunstgewerbemuseum der Stadt Köln*, Köln 1969, p.98f, fig.113.
Cologne, Wallraf-Richartz Museum, no.WRM336.

Cologne Master of around 1420

4. The Virgin and Child in a Meadow

The Virgin sits in a flowery meadow in front of a wood. With her right hand she supports the Christ Child in her lap who looks up at her. In her left hand she holds a carnation with a delicate gesture and slightly inclines her head to the left. The background is gilt, the Virgin's halo and the margin – as well as the frame proper – are of repoussé work.

The little panel and its frame are made from the same piece of wood. The subject of the Virgin and Child in a meadow was very popular in Cologne and was often painted, particularly in the workshops connected with the Master of St. Veronica, the Master of St. Lawrence and Stephan Lochner. The motif was further developed in pictures showing the Virgin in a garden of paradise, or in a rose-bower. This Madonna is human and modest, she is not the enthroned Queen of Heaven. The picture was clearly meant for private prayer and meditation. The carnation in the Virgin's hand makes symbolic reference both to herself and to Christ's Passion (legend has it that the first carnation grew where the Virgin's tears dropped on the path to Golgotha). The little picture has been attributed to the Master of St. Veronica and also to the Master of the Wasservass Altarpiece, but technique, composition and many details make it unlikely that either of these two masters painted it. It is the work of a master of around 1420 who is as yet unknown and whose work has not yet been closely examined.

Oak, 18 × 12·5cm (7 × 5in). Old frame. In the Virgin's halo: *sancta ma.*
Acquired for the Museum in 1856, from the Collection of Joseph Essingh, Cologne.
Literature: Paul Pieper, *Zum Werk des Meisters der Hl. Veronika*, in: *Festschrift für Gert von der Osten*, Köln 1970, p.97; Stange, no.85; Katalog '*Rhein und Maas. Kunst und Kultur 800–1400*', Cologne 1972, p.419, no.Q22m.; Cologne Exhib., 1974, no.43.
Cologne, Wallraf-Richartz Museum, no.WRM337.

5. Parts of an Altarpiece   Four scenes of Christ's suffering and the *Last Judgement* are shown.

1. *The Agony of the Garden.* Christ prays and turns to the right where the cup stands on the rock. ('My Father, if it be possible, let this cup pass from me.' An angel holding a cross flies down. On shelves of rock in the foreground sit or lie the three sleeping disciples John, Peter and James the Great. The picture illustrates Christ's fear of death, as it is recorded by Matthew XXVI,36–46.

2. *Christ before Pilate.* Pontius Pilate sits on a canopied throne. To the right a servant kneels on a step before the throne and offers Pilate a jug of water and a bowl. The scene shows the defenceless Christ surrounded by a horde of soldiers and is based on Matthew XXVII,11–26.

3. *The Flagellation and the Crowning with Thorns.* The small figures in niches above the main openings and above the capital of the central pillar are presumably idols and figures from Jewish history; on the upper wall are invented Hebrew letters.
     In the left-hand room Christ is beaten by soldiers. In the right-hand room two soldiers press the crown of thorns on his head, one mocks him, another kneels down and mockingly offers him a branch for a sceptre. The scenes are based on Matthew XXVII,27–31.

4. *Descent from the Cross.* On the middle ladder stands the rich Joseph of Arimathaea who receives Christ's corpse in a shroud. Several other helpers are on the right-hand ladder and on the ground. One of Christ's followers pulls the nail out of his feet with a pair of pincers. In the foreground on the left St. John supports the Virgin who reaches out with her hands to hold the right arm of the dead Christ. The scene is based on Matthew XXVII,57–60.

5. *Last Judgement.* Christ sits enthroned on a double rainbow, above sun and moon. He shows his stigmata and lowers his left hand towards the damned, while his right hand is raised for the saved. The symbolic sword and palm on either side of his halo correspond to these two gestures. From the clouds above him angels carry the instruments of the Passion and Redemption, the so-called *arma Christi*: the pillar of the flagellation, the cross, lance, reed and sponge, the rod, nails and bowl of vinegar. Slightly below Christ at either side of him the Virgin and St. John the Baptist kneel on clouds, praying and interceding for the mortals. Angels look down from clouds below Christ and blow the trumpets of the Last Judgement. Below them, the dead rise from their graves, men, a woman and a monk. In the foreground on the lower left St. Peter can be seen leading the saved to the portal of paradise while on the other side devils drive the damned to the mouth of hell. Heaven and earth are clearly set apart, the one having a gilt ground, the other a natural sky.

5. *Continued*

A panel showing the *Taking of Christ* (in the Suermondt Museum in Aachen), originally belonged to the set of these five panels. Two pictures showing the *Entombment* and the *Resurrection* also belonged (Kaiser–Friedrich Museum, Berlin up to 1945; lost in the war). Together they formed two wings of an altarpiece whose centre panel is so far unidentified. The panels were presumably sawn apart at the beginning of the 19th century. The centre panel presumably showed a *Crucifixion*. The sequence follows a well-known Cologne pattern – it recurs on the wing of the St. Lawrence altarpiece (see no.8) for instance. But as far as painting style is concerned the master of this panel is an individualist. The emotional power of his narratives and the elongated and twisted figures reflect a more expressionist style than is usual for Cologne. His known *œuvre* is small. The panels have occasionally been attributed to the Master of St. Veronica, but more recently scholars have agreed that they could be connected with the Older Master of the Holy Kindred. It is probable that the painter of these panels started off in the workshop of this older master and went on to develop a highly individual style.

Oak, 75 × 46cm (2ft 5½in × 1ft 6⅛in) each panel.
No.3 from the Schnütgen Collection; the others from the Wallraf-Collection.
Literature: Otto H. Förster, *Um den Meister der Veronika*, in: *Wallraf-Richartz-Jahrbuch*, XIX, 1957, p.230ff, fig.159–163; E. G. Grimme, *Das Suermondt-Museum, Aachen*, in: *Aachener Kunstblätter*, 28, 1963, p.218, no.118, abb.219.

The Master of Saint Veronica

(active in the first quarter of the 15th century)

This anonymous artist is named from a painting showing *St. Veronica with the Sudarium* (Munich, Alte Pinakothek no.11866, see opposite) owned, in the early 19th century, by the brothers Boisserée. It was said by them to come from the church of St. Severin, Cologne.

Attempts have been made to identify the Master with the names of artists recorded in Cologne, like Master Wilhelm and Hermann Wynrich of Wesel. None of these identifications has gained general acceptance.

The Master was the most important painter in Cologne before the time of Stephan Lochner. He still demonstrates the gentle atmosphere and delicate modelling of the so-called 'soft style'; this is allied with the elegance and preciosity of the International Gothic movement. The Master's sense of colour is, however, highly individual, as is his particular way of infusing iconic compositions with naturalism and, at times, drama.

6. Saint Veronica
with the Sudarium

Saint Veronica displays to the spectator the cloth with which she wiped the face of Christ, and upon which his image (the 'true image' or 'vera icon') miraculously appeared (see Index of Saints: Veronica). Christ's halo is inscribed *ihs.xps.ihs.x* (for *Jesus Christus*). The Saint's halo identifies her with the inscription *sancta veronica*. In the gold on either side of her head are pounced small angels fluttering in 'pie-crust' clouds (more readily visible since the painting was cleaned in 1976).

The frontal, symmetrical disposition of Christ's head and its dark modelling has prompted scholars to trace its derivation to Byzantine sources. It would appear that the painting is complete as it stands and, as such, probably used for private prayer.

This panel has been continually compared with that in Munich from which the Master takes his name, and upon which attributions rest. The Munich picture shows Christ's head crowned with thorns; in addition, two groups of three angels occupy a chequered floor. The National Gallery picture, which is by far the smaller, omits the angels and floor. It presents a more tightly framed, less discursive image. The head of Christ is shown without the crown of thorns and bears no marks of torture or suffering, and may relate to another part of the St. Veronica legend.

Levey described the picture as belonging to the Circle of the Master of Saint Veronica. It is remarkable, however, that its pounced border is exactly comparable to that of the Munich painting, as are other aspects of its technical make-up. These considerations would certainly confirm the origin of both paintings in the same workshop. Zehnder affirmed that both were painted by the same hand. The recent cleaning has fully revealed the high quality of the painting which may now be seen to equal that of the Munich painting. This results in a new situation whereby the Master's hand may be identified from the London panel with as much justification as from the Munich one.

Walnut, painted surface, $44 \cdot 2 \times 33 \cdot 7$cm (1ft $5\frac{3}{8}$in × 1ft $1\frac{1}{4}$in). The unpainted wood surrounding the painted surface displays, at regular intervals, holes made by nails which would have held in place the original (?) frame. The gold background displays slight wear. Cleaned in 1976.
From the church of St. Lawrence, Cologne (demolished in 1817). Purchased for the National Gallery in 1862, as by 'Master Wilhelm'.
Literature: Levey, p.95; Stange no.41 (as a copy after the Munich *St. Veronica*); F.G. Zehnder, *Der Meister der H. Veronika*, unpublished dissertation at Bonn 1973; Cologne Exhib., 1974, no.17.
London, National Gallery, no.687.

7. 'The Small Calvary' The three crosses bearing Christ and the two robbers stand in a landscape, under a sky showing both sun and moon. Angels surround Christ's cross in the centre; they mourn, pray and receive his blood in chalices. Beside and beneath the cross are several noble horsemen, among them the 'good captain' and the blind Longinus, who pierces Christ's side with a spear. To the lower left is a group of mourning women with St. John; they support the fainting Virgin. To the lower right men are seen arguing; soldiers cast lost for Christ's tunic. In the centre beneath the cross a soldier removes the bowl of vinegar and the reed and sponge.

 This is one of the main works of the Master of St. Veronica. It is a devotional picture belonging to the type of 'crowded' Calvary where the crucifixion of Christ is narrated with greater epic breadth than usual. For models one must look to French illuminated manuscripts of around 1400. A miniature in a missal in the library of Heidelberg University (MS Salem 9A, fol.99) is even more closely related. The *Crucifixion* panel almost seems an enlarged version, on wood, of a page in an illuminated manuscript.

Oak, 50·5 × 37·5cm (1ft 8in × 1ft 2¾in). On the scroll of the good captain: *Vere filius Dei erat iste*; on the back of the panel: WINAND GVLIG.
In the possession of Winand Gülich (middle of the 17th century); Lassaulx Collection, Coblenz; Dietz Collection, Coblenz; Clemens Collection, Aachen. Bought by the Wallraf-Richartz–Museum, Cologne, in 1912.
Literature: Stange, no.36; Zehnder, 1973, p.95f, cat. no.9; Cologne Exhib., 1974, no.16.
Cologne, Wallraf-Richartz Museum, no.WRM11.

| The Master of St. Lawrence | This important anonymous master of Cologne gothic painting was given his name after the right-hand wing of an altarpiece whose inner panel is in the Wallraf-Richartz Museum in Cologne (see no.8), while the sawn-off outer side of the same panel, showing the *Entombment of St. Lawrence*, is in the *Germanisches Nationalmuseum* in Nuremberg. This altarpiece was originally in the parish church of St. Lawrence in Cologne (now demolished). The Master was influenced by the Master of St. Veronica; he may even have been his successor in the workshop and may have collaborated on his late works. He may have been trained in Westphalia and only came to Cologne when already an experienced painter. His works date from about 1415 to about 1430. |

8. Altar panel with the *Death* and the *Coronation of the Virgin,* and the *Resurrection* and *Ascension of Christ*
See cover plate

In the picture on the upper left, the mourning apostles are shown sitting or crouching around the bed of the Virgin. In a roundel above, Christ receives the soul of the Virgin. In the picture on the upper right, Christ crowns his mother and gives her the sceptre of heaven. Singing angels sit in the lower corners of the picture, while two more angels playing musical instruments stand on either side of Christ and the Virgin. The heavenly background is similar to a garden of paradise.

The picture on the lower left shows the moment of resurrection, with the figure of Christ hovering above the sarcophagus, holding the banner of the cross, while the four guards sleep. The picture on the lower right shows Christ's ascension when, leaving the earth, he leaves his footprints. The Virgin and the apostles are shown praying, with their faces raised to heaven.

All scenes, except that of the *Resurrection*, are appropriately framed at the top with the arch of heaven, in which angels can be seen.

This panel, together with its sawn-off and cut-down outer side (*Entombment of St. Lawrence*, Germanisches Nationalmuseum, Nuremberg, Inv. no.Gm6), was originally the right wing of an altarpiece in the parish church of St. Lawrence in Cologne. The other panels of the altarpiece are missing; but it is most likely that the sequence went on with further scenes from the lives of the Virgin and Christ on the inner sides, while the lost outer side of the left wing presumably showed the *Martyrdom of St.Lawrence*. The quality of the individual scenes on the panel varies, the *Ascension* in particular shows weaknesses in the execution.

There are similarities with the works of the Master of St. Veronica (e.g. angels on the Veronica panel in Munich: see p.31).

Oak, 190 × 120cm (6ft 3in × 3ft 11¼in). Names in the haloes of the Virgin and the apostles. Restored 1949.
From the Church of St. Lawrence, Cologne; Collection Freiherr von Haxthausen; Collection Freiherr von Brenken; Schnütgen Collection; transferred from the Schnütgen Museum.
Literature: Stange no.45; Zehnder, 1973, p.118ff, cat.no.13; Cologne Exhib., 1974, no.25. Cologne, Wallraf-Richartz Museum, no.737.

9. The Madonna in the
Garden of Paradise

The Madonna sits among the flowers of a meadow which is bordered by a low
wall; the child is on her lap. Her crown distinguishes her as the Queen of
Heaven. Two angels kneel to her right and offer a psaltery to the child, who
plucks at the strings.

Obviously a devotional picture, used for private prayer and meditation. The
enclosed garden (*hortus conclusus*) was a very popular motif in Rhenish art,
particularly in Cologne. In Cologne painting generally, the Madonna is often
shown in the open air (see no.4). But the scene in the present picture is a highly
individual variant of the idyll of mother and child in paradise: it is a genre scene
which ingeniously combines the motif of the garden of paradise with that of
angelic music; the psaltery has a special symbolic connection with Christ. A
miniature from the Boucicaut workshop (Paris, Bibl.Nat., lat.1161, fol.130v)
and a Paris miniature (Paris, Bibl.Nat., ms.lat.924, fol.241r) are considered to be
among the models for this panel. It was formerly attributed to the Master of
St. Veronica, but there are many reasons for incorporating it into the *œuvre* of the
St. Lawrence Master. There are similarities to the panel of the Virgin from the
altarpiece from St. Lawrence's (see no.8) and also to a triptych in the Kisters
Collection in Kreuzlingen.

Oak, 19 × 15cm (7½ × 6in). In the halo of the madonna: *sancta maria ma*. Restored in 1976.
Original location unknown; German private collection; Dr. Peter Ludwig, Aachen; on
loan to the Wallraf-Richartz Museum since 1976.
Literature: Alfred Stange, *Ein Paradiesgärtchen vom Meister der Hl. Veronika*, in: *Pantheon*, 18,
1960. p.142; E. M. Vetter, *Das Frankfurter Paradiesgärtlein*, in: *Heidelberger Jahrbücher 9*,
1965, p.114, fig.8; Zehnder, 1973, p.133f, cat.no.14; Cologne Exhib., 1974, no.24.
Cologne, on loan to the Wallraf-Richartz Museum from the Dr. Peter Ludwig Collection,
Aachen.

10. 'The Large Passion'   Six scenes from Christ's Passion are shown. *Upper row*: *The Agony in the Garden,
Christ before the High Priest*, the *Flagellation*.   Lower row: *Christ being Crowned
with Thorns, Christ Carrying the Cross*, the *Crucifixion*. The donor, in a black
cloak with a fur lining, kneels at the bottom of the *Crucifixion* panel and his two
sons, in the habit of Dominican monks, kneel behind him.

   This is the inner side of the left wing of an altarpiece; a corresponding right
wing is also in the Wallraf-Richartz Museum in Cologne. It shows the remaining
scenes of the Passion. Upper row: *Resurrection, Noli me tangere, Ascension*.
Lower row: *Descent from the Cross* and *Christ in limbo*. A scene of the *Entombment*
which was originally part of the lower row was lost in the war. The scene of the
Descent from the Cross includes the wife of the donor with her two daughters who
are dressed as nuns of the order of St. Clare. The outer side of this left-hand wing
(which has been cut off) showed Saints Stephen, Lawrence, Giles and Eligius
with the kneeling donor and his sons, dressed as Dominican monks. (Lost by the
Wallraf-Richartz Museum during the war.) The outer side of the right wing
may have shown St. Louis of Toulouse, St. Francis, and the Virgin with St. John.
Fragments of this panel were formerly in the Schnütgen Museum and in the
Merlo Collection in Cologne. The centre panel is presumed lost; we do not
know whether it was a painting or a carved panel, nor do we know its subject.

   This panel is generally attributed to the Master of St. Lawrence. Indeed,
individual scenes recur in his work (e.g. *Resurrection* and *Ascension* in the altar
panel from St. Lawrence, see no.8); as do the choice of colours, conception of
figures and draperies, and the reticent narrative style, expressed in sparse gestures.
Among the *œuvre* of the Master of St. Lawrence this panel must be regarded as a
late work.

Oak, each 88 × 53·5cm to 56cm (2ft 10½in × 1ft 9in); size of whole wing 190 × 170cm
(6ft 2¾in × 5ft 7in). Names in the haloes of Christ, the Apostles, the Virgin and the Holy
Women. Restored 1969–70.
Collection Johann Georg Schmitz, Cologne. Bought by the Wallraf-Richartz Museum in
1846.
Literature: Stange, no.46; Zehnder, 1973, p.118ff, cat.no.15; Cologne Exhib., 1974, no.26.
Cologne, Wallraf-Richartz Museum, nos.20–25.

Stephan Lochner
(born *c.*1410?–died 1451)

Born probably at Meersburg on Lake Constance. First recorded in Cologne in 1442, working on decorations for the visit of Emperor Frederick III. In 1447 he was elected a councillor of the painters' guild. He was awarded the most important commission of the century—the 15-foot-wide triptych showing the *Adoration of the Magi*, painted for the Town Hall chapel, now in the Cathedral (see Index of Saints: Three Magi). This altarpiece was seen in 1520 by Albrecht Dürer, who referred to it as by 'maister Steffan zu Köln'. One of his pictures bears the date 1445 (*Presentation*, Gulbenkian Coll.); another is dated 1447 (*Presentation*, Darmstadt). Lochner died in 1451, a year in which Cologne suffered from the plague. Lochner was the most important Cologne painter of his time, balancing in his work a new realism (perhaps learned in the Netherlands) with a deep mysticism and rich, almost expressionist, use of colour.

11. Saints Matthew, Catherine of Alexandria and John the Evangelist

On the reverse: St. Jerome, A Female Martyr and St. Gregory the Great with a kneeling donor wearing the cloak of a Knight of Malta.

St. Matthew is accompanied by the angel who is believed to have dictated him his Gospel. St. Catherine has the wheel which was split by divine intervention when she was being tortured on it; she holds the sword which eventually killed her; she wears a crown, since she was reputed to be a queen. It is unusual that she wears around her neck a Tau-cross and bell; these attributes are usually associated with St. Anthony Abbot (the Hermit). In some versions of her legend, St. Catherine is said to have learned her faith from a hermit; this may explain the use of these attributes here.

St. John the Evangelist carries about his waist a pen in its case, and an ink-well; the eagle is the symbol of the inspiration which helped him write the Book of Revelation while exiled on Patmos. He holds a chalice from which rears a serpent; a legend relates that he drank from a poisoned cup, and survived because of his faith. By extension, the chalice also stands for the Christian faith; the serpent represents the devil.

On the reverse: St. Gregory's inspirational dove is poised at his ear. The female martyr is possibly St. Cordula, rather than Ursula (see Index of Saints: Cordula). The painting is the left-hand wing of an altarpiece; for the right-hand wing see no.12. The now-damaged surfaces would originally have been on the outside, showing the Four Fathers of the Church, two female Saints and the two donors. The inner sides displayed the Four Evangelists with Saints Catherine and Barbara. The centre of the altar is lost, and its form unknown.

The attribution to Lochner is universally accepted. Levey tentatively suggests a date after 1445.

Oak, painted surface, 68·6 × 58·1cm (2ft 3in × 1ft 10⅞in). Cut down at top and bottom. The reverse is considerably damaged. (Cleaned in 1970).
The presence of the Knights of Malta suggests that the altarpiece would most likely have been made for the Cologne church associated with that Order, namely Saints John and Cordula. Acquired by the Boisserée brothers and exchanged by them with Count Joseph von Rechberg. Thence to the Oettingen-Wallerstein collection which was bought by Prince Albert, the Prince Consort, in 1848. Given to the National Gallery by Queen Victoria, at the Prince Consort's wish, 1863. *Literature*: Levey, p.59; Stange, no.93.
London, National Gallery, no.705.

12. Saints Mark,
Barbara and Luke

Two panels displayed back to back. *On the 'reverse'*: St. Ambrose in pontifical robes and mitre, with book and cross-staff; St. Cecilia with a book, martyr's palm and a wreath of flowers in her hair; St. Augustine in pontifical robes and mitre, with his crozier and a pierced heart. This last attribute usually served to distinguish Ambrose and Augustine from each other. In front of Ambrose kneels the donor in the robes of the Knights of Malta.

St. Mark is accompanied by his lion; St. Barbara holds a small tower, her martyr's palm and wears a wreath of flowers in her hair; St. Luke has his ox, and a picture of the Virgin in his right hand (which identifies him as the first man to paint her).

These two panels were originally the front and back of one (right-hand) wing of an altarpiece which was sawn apart in 1824–6. The corresponding left wing is in the National Gallery in London (see no.11). The donor shown in the picture has his name, *Fr. Heynricus Zeuwelgyn*, inscribed on the facing; he wears the robes of the Knights of Malta. The Zeuwelgyn family lived and owned property in Lövenich near Cologne. The donor Heinrich Zeuwelgyn was the son of Heinrich Zeuwelgyn and his wife Aleid, *née* von Mauenheim. After the elder Zeuwelgyn's death his widow sold part of her property to the Order of Malta in 1386. The Cologne Knights of Malta lived according to the rules established by St. Augustine, who is shown in the picture.

Oak, 105 × 57·5cm (3ft 5¼in × 1ft 10½in), reverse: 86 × 58cm (2ft 9¾in × 1ft 10¾in).
On the bottom of the outer side: *Fr. heynricus zeuwelgyn· laycus.*
From the Wallraf Collection.
Literature: J. H. Emminghaus, *Lukas (Heilige in Bild und Legende)*, Recklinghausen 1966, p.65, fig.55; Jürgen Schultze, *Markus (Heilige in Bild und Legende)*, Recklinghausen 1966, p.43, fig.21; Stange, no.93; Levey, The German School (National Gallery Catalogues), London 1959, p.60ff.
Cologne, Wallraf-Richartz Museum, nos. WRM68 and 69.

The Master of the Life of the Virgin

(active in the second half of the 15th century)

This anonymous painter is named from a series of eight paintings which show various scenes from the Life of the Virgin. Seven are in the Alte Pinakothek, Munich; one, the *Presentation in the Temple* is in the National Gallery (no.13). Some have claimed that the panels originally formed an altarpiece with wings, but recent technical evidence suggests that each was created as an individual unit, and that they would have been displayed as a narrative cycle. One panel shows a donor, probably Johann von Hirtz (Councillor in Cologne 1440–74, died 1481), who endowed a chapel in the church of St. Ursula, from where the paintings stem.

The Master was the most influential Cologne painter of his time. His style suggests that he may well have been trained in the Netherlands, rather than learning from Netherlandish pictures imported into Cologne; e.g. Rogier van der Weyden's altarpiece in St. Columba's.

His linear style has much of the lyricism and pathos of Bouts, from whom he clearly learned gesture and facial expression.

13. The Presentation in
the Temple

The scene portrayed is from St. Luke ch. 11,22ff. '*And when the days of her purifi-
cation according to the law of Moses were accomplished, they brought him to Jerusalem,
to present him to the Lord; And to offer a sacrifice according to that which is said in the
law of the Lord, A pair of turtledoves, or two young pigeons.*' A young woman is seen
on the left, holding the doves. The actual moment depicted is that when Simeon,
to whom it was revealed '*that he should not see death before he had seen the Lord's
Christ*', takes the child Jesus from the Virgin and declares '*Lord, now lettest thou thy
servant depart in peace. . . . For mine eyes have seen thy salvation.*' The prominence of
the candles, one of which St. Joseph (on left) is preparing to light, is probably in
reference to Simeon's next words which describe the Infant as '*A light to lighten
the Gentiles*', a statement which points the contrast between physical and
spiritual illumination.

The Virgin's halo bears traces of a pounced inscription. Simeon's cape shows,
in embroidery, some figures of prophets (cf. nos.18,55 in this exhibition) and, on
the dorsal, the Emperor Augustus being shown a miraculous vision of the Virgin
and Child by the Tiburtine Sibyl (a parallel to the revelation now being vouch-
safed to Simeon). This typological parallel is also seen in the retable on the altar.
Two scenes reflect the theme of sacrifice (*Offering of Cain and Abel* together with
the *Murder of Abel*, the latter a reference to Christ's future Passion; the *Sacrifice of
Isaac*). The third, the *Drunkenness of Noah* traditionally refers to Christ's nakedness during his flagellation, but here also provides a contrast with the innocent
nakedness of the Child.

The artist has attempted to lend the altar an air of Eastern authenticity, by
giving the supporting figures some suggestion of oriental appearance. The two
clean-shaven figures in the background appear to be in contemporary dress and
may be portraits.

The picture is one of the series from which the Master takes his name. Although
it has been suggested that it was executed by an assistant, known as the Master of
the Lyversberg Passion, this view is not acceptable. When one takes into account
the fact that most painters of the time made use of teams of assistants there seems
to be no real case for doubting the attribution of the series to one unifying Master.
The cycle's data is generally accepted as being early within the Master's production, around 1460/65.

Oak, painted surface, 84 × 108·5cm (2ft 9in × 3ft 6¾in), cleaned in 1957.
Originally in the church of St. Ursula, Cologne. In the collection of the Boisserée brothers,
Heidelberg, by March 1812. Then as for no.11.
Literature: Levey, p.85; Stange, no.167; H. Schmidt, *Der Meister des Marienlebens und sein
Kreis*, unpublished dissertation presented at Bonn, 1969; Goldberg and Scheffler, p.307.
London, National Gallery, no. 706.

14. The Vision of Saint
Bernard

The Virgin wears a wreath of flowers in her hair, in her left hand she holds a red carnation, with her right hand she squeezes milk from her breast towards St. Bernard. The saint wears the Cistercian habit. With his right hand he touches the legs of the Infant Christ.

The saint was founder of the Cistercian Order (see Index of Saints). The miracle shown in this picture is supposed to have happened in the church of St Vorles in Chatillon-sur-Seine when St. Bernard was praying in front of a statue of the Virgin: '*Monstra te esse matrem*'. The statue is then supposed to have moved and pressed on her breast so that drops of milk moistened the lips of the saint which were dry from prayer. The carnation in the Virgin's hand is a symbol of Christ's death on the cross.

The small panel must surely have been used for private prayer. The composition, starting in the lower left-hand corner with the Infant Christ and leading on to the two half-figures of the Virgin and saint, shows the hand of a master. The faces, landscape and general delineation of the figures all point to the Master of the Life of the Virgin, and his authorship has never been doubted. The picture is a mature work and must have been done around 1480.

Oak, 31·3 × 24·5cm (1ft ⅜in × 9⅝in). Inscriptions punched in the haloes. Restored in 1930 and 1953.
First known in the collection of J. B. Ciolina-Zanoli (died 1837) Cologne; then Collection Clavé von Bouhaben; acquired in 1894.
Literature: O. H. Förster, *Das Wallraf-Richartz-Museum in Köln*, Cologne 1961, p.21, fig.50; Stange, no.178; *Kindlers Malerei Lexikon*, IV, 1967, p.305ff, fig.307; E. G. Grimme, *Unsere Liebe Frau*, Cologne 1968, cat.no.76; H. Schmidt, *Studien zur spätgotischen Malerei in Köln. Der Meister des Marienlebens und sein Kreis*. Diss. Bonn 1969.
Cologne, Wallraf-Richartz Museum, no.WRM128.

The Master of the Life
of the Virgin (?)

15. A King and an
Attendant

The young companion of the kings is shown in contemporary dress with sword, dagger and belt-pouch. Under his short coat he wears fashionable hose and boots with spurs. His stance suggests that he has just jumped off the horse behind him and is now forcing it to stand still.

The two panels are parts of altarpiece wings, which were sawn apart after 1824. In the 1824 catalogue of the Early German School they are still listed as complete wings. The original altarpiece had four wings; its centre panel is lost. The inner sides of the wings showed the three holy kings and an attendant—one king and the attendant are the panels exhibited here. The outer sides showed *Christ as Redeemer* (formerly the reverse of the king exhibited here), *St. Egidius*, the *Virgin of the Annunciation* (formerly the reverse of the attendent) and the *Angel of the Annunciation*. This iconography surely demanded a *Virgin and Child* in the centre. Whether this centre panel was painted or carved, however, remains uncertain. The plinth-like floors of the wings and the statuesque figures suggest that it was carved.

The other wings of the altarpiece are also in the Wallraf-Richartz Museum. Their inner sides, including the two panels exhibited here, have always been regarded as autograph works by the Master. The panels have been connected with the wings of the Tersteegen altarpiece and dated to around 1490 (Stange). Other paintings done in the Master's workshop could also be considered. Very recently, it has been claimed (Schmidt) that the panels could be the work of the Master of the Legend of St George who may have painted the donor wings of the Tersteegen altarpiece.

Oak, 172×39cm each (5ft 7¾in × 1ft 3¼in). Restored in 1957.
From the Wallraf Collection.
Literature: Catalogue '*Tiere in der Kunst*', Wallraf-Richartz Museum, Cologne 1967, p.17, no.5; Stange, no.180; H. Schmidt, *Studien zur spätgotischen Malerei in Köln. Der Meister des Marienlebens und sein Kreis.* Diss. Bonn 1969; Cologne Exhib., 1970, no.8.
Cologne, Wallraf-Richartz Museum, nos.WRM129 and 135.

16. A pair of wings from an altarpiece

(a) The Conversion of Saint Hubert.

(b) Saints Augustine, Ludger (?), Hubert and Gereon (?).

(c) The Mass of Saint Hubert.

(d) Saints Jerome, Bernard (?), Giles and Benedict (?).

The paintings formed wings of an altarpiece in the Benedictine abbey church at Werden on the Ruhr. Panel (*a*) was the inside left wing, (*b*) the outside left wing; (*c*) was the inside right wing, (*d*) the outside right wing. It is not known what the other constituents of the altar comprised. In (*a*), St. Hubert's conversion is portrayed (see Index of Saints: Hubert). While out hunting he was confronted by a stag bearing a Crucifix between its antlers; he thereupon gave up his worldly pursuits. In (*c*) there is seen a scene rarely mentioned in documentations of the Saint's life. St. Hubert is shown as a bishop, his mitre and crozier held by a kneeling deacon; an angel appears with a stole for him. The presence of the dog refers to St. Hubert's role as a protector against hydrophobia. The retable shows God the Father between Saints Peter and Paul.

The paintings were described by their first owner as by the 'Master of Werden' since the panels came from the abbey there. Subsequently, all scholars have given them to one master or another in the circle dominated by the Master of the Life of the Virgin. Most recently, Schmidt has ascribed them to the painter of a diptych (Bonn, Landesmuseum). This has some of the Westphalian characteristics of the National Gallery paintings, but its extremely small scale precludes proper comparison.

Certainly, the outsides of the wings are by a less accomplished hand than the inner narrative scenes. The two narrative scenes have also been thought to be by different hands. Levey emphasises the quality of the *Conversion* and affirms its authorship by the Master of the Life of the Virgin, and ascribes the wings to the Master's 'Studio'. The panels are generally thought to be of about 1485/90.

Panels (*a*) and (*b*) still have the original oak support; (*c*) and (*d*) had been transferred to canvas and were laid down on a synthetic panel in 1974/6 when all four panels were cleaned. The painted surfaces measure 123·8 × 82·5cm (4ft 4¾in × 2ft 6½in) approx.
Originally in the abbey at Werden on the Ruhr, the paintings were in the collection of Carl Wilhelm August Krüger (1797–1868) at Minden by 1847. The collection was purchased for the Gallery in 1854, after being inspected, for the nation, by William Dyce, R.A.
Literature: Levey, p.87; Manchester Exhib., 1961, no.7 (as Master of the Life of the Virgin or his studio); Stange, no.159 (as by the Master of the St. George Legend); H. Schmidt, *Der Meister des Marienlebens und sein Kreis*, unpublished dissertation presented at Bonn, 1969 (as by the Master of the Bonn Diptych); Cologne Exhib., 1970, no.16 (as by the Master of the Bonn Diptych); W. Koenig, *Studien zum Meister von Liesborn*, 1974, nos. 26–29.
London, National Gallery, nos.250–253.

The Master of the
Glorification of the
Virgin (?)

17. St. Maurice and
Companions

This anonymous master was given his name from a painting of the *Glorification of the Virgin*, in the Wallraf-Richartz Museum in Cologne. Netherlandish influence and Cologne tradition clearly interact in his work. His figures and compositions are very close to Stephan Lochner and suggest that the master knew Lochner's works or even Lochner himself. On the other hand, the colouring, spatial arrangements and, above all, the landscapes point towards the Netherlands, particularly to Rogier van der Weyden. The Master is the first Cologne painter who pained landscapes with enthusiasm. His figures are majestic, enveloped in robes, heavy and sculptural. But he paid as much attention to the details of a landscape as to details of figures and draperies.

Many paintings have been attributed to him. Stylistic features suggest that the master worked in Cologne from the sixth decade of the 15th century onwards. It is not yet clear whether he was active only up to 1470–80 or up to as late as 1493. Similarly there is no proof that he is identical with the painter Goedart Butgyn von Aiche (d.1490) who is mentioned several times in Cologne after 1463, although this has been suggested by scholars.

St. Maurice is emphasised by his large halo and golden armour. Behind him and to the right a number of nobly dressed and armoured companions of varying ages follow him. In the lower right-hand corner kneels the donor, a middle-class woman, with her coat-of-arms (as yet unidentified).

On the back are fragments of the lower part of the Virgin's robe. The panel was originally the lower part of the right-hand wing of an altarpiece. The corresponding upper part of this wing is in the *Germanisches Nationalmuseum* in Nuremberg and shows *St. Gereon and his Companions*. On the back of the Nuremberg panel is the upper part of the figure of the Virgin praying. The corresponding left-hand wing of the altarpiece belongs to the Wallraf-Richartz Museum. It shows the *Adoration of the Kings* at the top and *St. Ursula and her Companions* at the bottom. On the back of this panel is the angel of the Annunciation. The altarpiece thus originally showed the Annunciation when closed, and when open, saints who were particularly revered in Cologne with their companions. The centre panel is lost. The altarpiece was presumably split up at the beginning of the 19th century.

The master of this altarpiece was clearly influenced by Lochner's altarpiece of the Patron Saints of Cologne, now the main altarpiece in Cologne Cathedral. The painting technique and facial types of the St. Maurice panel are close to Lochner, but the overall style is more brittle and less assured. The painter presumably worked in close proximity to Lochner, perhaps even in his workshop; his art has its roots there. Stange attributed this panel and the others to a 'Master of 1456', while the paintings on the back were assumed to have been done by the Master

The Master of the Glorification of the Virgin (?)

17. *Continued*

of the Glorification of the Virgin. But it ought to be considered whether the paintings on the front as well as the back should not be attributed to this master, and whether the differences in quality and style could not simply be the result of the panels having been done at different times. Our panel should probably be dated to around 1460.

Oak, 82·5 × 90cm (2ft 8½in × 2ft 11½in). Restored in 1956.
Originally in the church of St. Bridget, Cologne; then Wallraf Collection.
Literature: E. Depel, *Das Kölner Dombild und die Lochnernachfolge um 1500*, in: *Kölner Domblatt*, 23, 1964, p.376; Stange, no.140.
Cologne, Wallraf–Richartz Museum, no.WRM87.

The Master of the
Glorification of the
Virgin

18. The Virgin and
Child with Saints Anne,
Christopher, Gereon
and Peter in a Landscape,
with Cologne and the
Siebengebirge
(in the background)

On the tiled floor in the foreground stand – from left to right – St.Christopher
with the Infant Christ on his shoulder, St. Gereon with his attributes of sword and
ensign, St. Peter as Pope in splendid liturgical robes and mitre, with cross-staff
and key, and the group of the Virgin, her mother Anne and the Christ child (see
Index of Saints). In the background is the panorama of Cologne, in front of it the
river Rhine with boats. In the extreme background are the mountains of the
Eifel, and to the left along the Rhine can be seen Brühl, Bonn, Siegburg and the
Siebengebirge (the 'Seven Mountains').

The panel was originally the inner side of the wing of an altarpiece. The corresponding outer side, shows the saints Francis, Bonaventura, Bernard and Clare
in front of Cologne seen from the west (Wallraf-Richartz Museum, no.WRM121).
As a note by Ramboux (the curator of the Museum) in the 1864 catalogue shows,
the wing was split under his supervision.

This master is still influenced by the motif, popular in 14th-century Cologne
painting, of arranging the saints in one long row. The draperies are painstakingly
rendered, the details of those of St. Christopher and St. Peter are very precisely
drawn and must be based on a study from nature.

The landscape of Cologne and its southerly and westerly surroundings (which
are largely topographically correct) is very charming indeed. This is the first
complete, scarcely-distorted view of Cologne, in which both the general layout
and the individual buildings can be seen. Cologne is no longer the city of monu-
ments it had been in a canvas of around 1441 (no.WRM51) but a bourgeois town
where trade flourishes and many people and their houses can be seen. There is
general agreement that the picture was painted by the Master himself, but the
date remains uncertain. On stylistic grounds it could have been painted around
1470/80, but the topography of Cologne and Brühl suggests a date after 1493.

Oak, 131 × 146cm (4ft 3½in × 4ft 9½in). Restored in 1951/2 and in 1968/9.
From the Wallraf Collection, Cologne.
Literature: P. Zilliken, *Eine mittelalterliche Brühler Stadtabbildung,* in: *Brühler Heimatblätter,*
1954, p.9ff, no.2; F. Wundisch, *Von alten Brühler Stadtansichten,* in: *Brühler Heimatblätter,*
1964, p.9, no.2; E. Depel, *Das Kölner Dombild und die Lochnernachfolge um 1500,* in: *Kölner
Domblatt,* 23, 1964, p.382, fig.7; Hans Schmidt, *Zum Werk des Meisters der Verherrlichung
Mariae,* in: *Schülerfestgabe für Herbert von Einem,* Bonn 1965, p.253ff, fig.8; Stange, no.145;
Unterricht in Museum (Hsg. G. v.d. Osten und B. Klesse), Schriften der Kölner Museen, I,
Köln 1970, p.187, fig.p.114.
Cologne, Wallraf-Richartz Museum, no.WRM120.

The name given to this prolific anonymous Cologne painter of around the turn
of the 16th century derives from his altarpiece now in the Wallraf-Richartz
Museum (see no.19); this is one of the main works of late gothic Cologne
painting of around 1500. His *œuvre* suggests that he was born around 1450 and
died around 1515. It is not known where he was trained; his work combines
Cologne traditions and Netherlandish influences.

There are no documents concerning this master, but works like the *Intercession*
altarpiece (*Germanisches Nationalmuseum*, Nuremberg) dated 1492, or the *Mass
of St. Gregory* (Diocesan Museum, Utrecht) dated 1486, provided fixed points
for a chronology.

The Master also worked for glass painters; the designs for the splendid north
windows of Cologne Cathedral can, for instance, be attributed to him. But it
remains doubtful whether he is identical – as has been maintained – with the
painter Lambert von Luytge who died in 1508.

19. Altarpiece of the
Holy Kindred
*See colour plate between
pp.154–5*

The centre panel shows the Virgin and Child with St. Anne enthroned under a
canopy. To the left of St. Anne sits St. Catherine, who holds out the betrothal
ring to the Child who turns towards her. On the other side sits St. Barbara
reading a book. In the lower left and right corners two women belonging to the
Holy Kindred and their children sit among the flowers of a meadow. In the upper
left corner is the *Presentation of the Virgin in the Temple*; in the upper right corner
the *Death of the Virgin*. Behind the seated women are the male members of the
Holy Kindred. The children read or play with utensils or attributes. The left inner
wing shows the Saints Roch and Nicasius with the donor Nicasius Hackeney in
an open landscape. *The Nativity* is inserted into the upper right corner like a
miniature. On the right wing Saints Gudula and Elisabeth stand in an open,
hilly landscape with buildings; they are accompanied by Christina Hackeney, *née*
Hardenrath, the wife of the donor. *The Assumption of the Virgin* is inserted in the
upper left corner. The outer side of the left wing shows St. Achatius and his
companions, and St. Leodegar, bishop of Autun, in a vaulted hall. In front of
them kneel the male members of the Hackeney family. The architectural setting
of the outer side of the right wing is a continuation of that of the outer left wing.
The saints Cecilia, Genovefa, Helena and an unknown saint, possibly Gertrude,
stand in front of a brocade curtain. In front of them the female members of the
Hackeney family kneel on the tiled floor.

The subject of the central panel is complex, several themes are treated at the
same time (see Index of Saints: Holy Kindred). The centre is taken up by the
group of the Virgin and Child with St. Anne; the independent motif of
St. Catherine's betrothal to the Infant Christ is skilfully connected with this
central group. The other figures are not identified, but presumably the man to the
right of the Virgin is Joseph. And the three other men are presumably Joachim,
Cleophas and Salome, the three husbands of St. Anne. The men behind
St. Barbara and St. Catherine may be their fathers.

The two other daughters are also shown in this picture: to the left Mary
Cleophas with her husband Alpheus (on the extreme left) and their children
James the Less, Barsabas, Simon Zelotes and Judas Thaddeus. In the lower right-

63

19. *Continued*

hand corner are Mary Salome with her husband Zebedee (on the extreme right) and their children St. John the Evangelist and James the Great. It is likely that the altarpiece was originally in the Achatius Nunnery in Cologne where the daughter of the Hackeney couple, Elisabeth, was a Dominican nun. This would explain the inclusion of St. Achatius on the outer side of the left wing. The donor Nicasius Hackeney was an accountant in the service of the Emperor Maximilian. As Christina Hackeney's first husband died in 1498 or 1499 the altarpiece cannot have been painted before 1500. But, on the other hand, the Hackeney coat-of-arms, granted by the Emperor Maximilian in 1504, does not yet appear, so the altarpiece must date from about 1500 to 1503.

It is generally agreed that the centre panel was painted by the master himself, while the wings, particularly their outer sides, show traces of the weaker hands of his apprentices.

Oak, 141 × 186cm (4ft 7½in × 6ft 1¼in) (centre panel), 141 × 85cm (4ft 7½in × 2ft 9½in) (each wing). Restored 1941.
From the Wallraf Collection, Cologne.
Literature: Stange, no.277; Ch. D. Cuttler, *Northern Painting*, New York 1968, p.278ff. R. Wallrath, *Meister der Heiligen Sippe*, in: *Kindlers Malerei Lexikon*, v, Zürich 1968, p.351ff, figs.352,353.
Cologne, Wallraf-Richartz Museum, no.WRM165.

20. Triptych: Saints Barbara and Dorothea with the Infant Christ

The wings of this small triptych have been put into one frame with the centre panel and can no longer be moved; the centre panel shows St. Barbara and St. Dorothea with the Christ Child. St. Barbara, wearing a crown and reading a book, stands on the left among the many flowers and plants of a meadow symbolizing the garden of paradise. Behind her is the tower in which her father held her captive. St. Dorothea stands to the right. In her left hand she holds a rose, in her right the basket of roses. (see Index of Saints).

On the left-hand wing the haloed figure of St. Bruno, carrying an olive branch, intercedes for a Carthusian monk. Mitre and crozier lie on the ground. Above the landscape, in the sky Maria Egyptica is carried upwards by angels.

On the right-hand wing the haloed figure of St. Hugh, holding his crozier, intercedes for a nun. In the background an open landscape with buildings can be seen. To the right is Maria Egyptica in a rock cave.

This little altarpiece is a typical Cologne work. But it should be noted that the centre panel has saints, rather than a scene from the Life of Christ or the Virgin. Presumably the two donors were brother and sister. The altarpiece may therefore have originated in a Carthusian or Carmelite monastery. As St. Bruno was canonized only in 1514 it must have been painted around 1514/15, that is in the master's last period.

Oak, 38 × 34cm (1ft 3in × 1ft 1½in) centre panel; 38 × 13·5cm (1ft 3in × 5¼in) each wing. Restored 1949.
From the Wallraf Collection.
Literature: A. Schröder, *Dorothea (Heilige in Bild und Legende),* Recklinghausen 1966, p.53, fig.p.51; Stange, no.286.
Cologne, Wallraf-Richartz Museum, no.WRM166.

The Master of the Saint Ursula Legend
(active in the late 15th/ early 16th century)

This anonymous painter is named after a series of paintings (19 are known) which tell the story of St. Ursula. They are datable (from the chronology of the donors) to about 1495–1505.

The paintings of the cycle were once given to the Master of St. Severin. There has been some discussion of the relative ages and roles of these two painters, who clearly demonstrate each other's influence. Although most of the pictures of the Ursula cycle are now cut down, some (Bonn, Landesmuseum) still possess their original architectural surrounds with tiny donors kneeling in each bottom corner.

The Master displays an innovatory treatment of distance and perspective and a thin, quickly-brushed technique very different from the layered colours of his predecessors. His paintings have canvas supports which is also an innovation in the context of the Cologne school of the 15th century; wooden panels were normally used.

21. The Martyrdom of Saint Ursula and the 11,000 Virgins

The scene shows the Saint in the centre supporting her bridegroom as he is pierced by the sword of an executioner. All around, virgins are put to the sword. The leader of the Huns, who has ordered the massacre, stands with his aides at the door of his tent. (See Index of Saints: Ursula).

The background shows the town of Cologne. Almost directly behind St. Ursula can be seen the flying buttresses of the unfinished cathedral. In the right background is the church of St. Gereon.

Below, are two pairs of donors, parts of whom have been cut away with the bottom of the canvas. They are identified (left) as Wynant van Wickroid and 'Lysbet syn hysfrau', and (right) Heinrich van Wickroid with *his* wife, Hilgen.

This painting is one of the 19 of the series from which the Master is named. It is double the width of any of the others and probably occupied the most important place within the cycle.

Canvas. 165 × 235cm (5ft 5in × 7ft 8½in). Cut at the bottom by about 8 inches.
The series was said to have been made for St. Bridget's in Cologne, but recently it has been suggested, with equal lack of proof, that it may have been for the Benedictine cloister of the Machabees. Bought for the Victoria & Albert Museum in 1857 'as an illustration of costume and ornament'.
Literature: C. M. Kauffmann, *The Legend of Saint Ursula*, 1964; Stange, no.297; Cologne Exhib., 1970, no.26c; C. M. Kauffmann, *Victoria & Albert Museum: Catalogue of Foreign Paintings*, 1973, p.184.
London, Victoria & Albert Museum, no.5938–1857.

Circle of the Master of the St. Ursula Legend

22. St. Lawrence shows the Treasures of the Church

St. Lawrence, as first archdeacon, had charge of the possessions of the Church. The Prefect of Rome imprisoned him in order to force him to tell the whereabouts of the Church treasures. After three days, St. Lawrence relented and took the Prefect to show him the hoard of riches. Indicating the poor and sick of Rome the saint declared 'These are the treasures of Christ's Church'. Whereupon, the Prefect had St. Lawrence martyred by means of roasting on a gridiron.

In the painting, the Prefect holds his staff upside-down, perhaps in emulation of the Roman 'thumb-down' death sentence. St. Lawrence stands next to him wearing the dalmatic. The man on the right wears, in his hat, badges from various places of pilgrimage.

The picture is one of a series showing scenes from the Life of St. Lawrence. Six of the original eight(?) survive. Some of the others bear coats-of-arms which may have been added later.

Technical examination of the National Gallery picture shows (beneath the visible paint surface) two sets of coats-of-arms and two scrolls which bear inscriptions. A first pair of coats-of-arms seems to have been replaced by a second pair. These items are painted in the bottom left- and right-hand corners; the presence of the scrolls can be discerned with the naked eye. Examination further suggests that large areas of the picture were re-painted at a very early date. This makes the relationship to the hand of the Ursula Master difficult to discern. It has been suggested that the original execution of the cycle is datable to about 1510.

Canvas, 130·2 × 92·7cm (4ft 3¼in × 3ft ½in).
From the Schwarzschild Collection, Warsaw. Presented to the National Gallery by Sir Henry Howarth, through the National Art-Collections Fund, in memory of Lady Howarth, 1922.
Literature: Levey, p.94; Stange, no.306.
London, National Gallery, no.3665.

The Master of St. Severin

This anonymous painter was named from two panels showing two saints each and from scenes of the legend of St. Severin in the church and vestry of the Cologne parish church of St. Severin. His *œuvre* is large, but the precise number and dates of his works have not yet been established. There are many links with the work of the Master of the St. Ursula Legend. There is general agreement among scholars that these two masters were the leading painters among a whole group. It may be that they worked in one workshop in which the Master of the St. Ursula Legend was the older master; he strongly influenced the Master of St. Severin.

The style of the Master of St. Severin clearly reflects Netherlandish influences; these may have been transmitted via the Master of St. Ursula, or he himself may have gone to the Netherlands (possibly to Leyden) during his journeying years. His early works are within the Cologne tradition. Only later does the hard, draughtsman-like style give way to a more painterly overall conception. This reflects the continuing influence of Lochner's works and also those of the Master of the Holy Kindred. His later works show a tendency towards almost grotesque faces.

It is thought that the Master of St. Severin also did designs for stained glass in Altenberg Abbey near Cologne, and for some in the north aisle of Cologne Cathedral. On the evidence of his works the master must have been born around 1460/5 and died around 1515/20. Whether he is identical with the city painter Master Clais, as has been said, remains uncertain.

23. An Old Woman

The woman holds prayer beads. The red background is very unusual. The picture may originally have formed the right wing of a diptych or triptych. If a diptych, the other panel would have shown the lady's husband; a triptych would have shown him in the left wing with a religious subject in the centre.

Perhaps painted around 1490.

Oak, 33·3 × 27cm (12 × 9⅛in).
First known in the Lyversberg collection, Cologne. Then Virnich Collection, Bonn. Acquired by the Hon. Mrs. Ronald Greville in 1927. Bequeathed by her to the National Trust in 1942.
Literature: Manchester Exhib., 1961, p.23, no.47; St. J. Gore, *Polesden Lacey*, 1964, p.19, no.23; Stange, no.320.
The National Trust, Polesden Lacey.

The Master of St. Severin

24. The Adoration of the Kings

The Virgin and Child sit enthroned in a ruined building. They turn towards one of the kings, presumably Caspar, who kneels before them.

The second king, Melchior, kneels to the right, holding his gift, a precious gold vessel, in his hands. The Moor Balthasar stands waiting on the extreme left; in his left hand he holds a golden goblet which a servant hands him. Behind the Virgin to the right stands Joseph, cap in hand.

For the subject, see Index of Saints: Three Magi. Lochner's altarpiece of the Patron Saints of Cologne, now the most important altarpiece in Cologne Cathedral, provided the principal model for this subject. But the Master's symmetry is less severe, the triangular composition made less rigid by the inclusion of Joseph and the black king acts as a counterbalance to the central group. The shifting of the figures makes the scene more private and intimate. A familiar, rather than majestic atmosphere is stressed. The brilliant colouring is well thought-out: the gold in the robes of the kings at the front, its relation to the pink and red of the curtain behind the Virgin, the three interacting greens reaching from the Moor to the Virgin and the man on the extreme right all reflect a very experienced use of colour. The motif of the pomegranate on the curtain refers to the Fall, Redemption and Empire of the World. It is already to be found in the Old Testament—pomegranates decorated the curtains of the temple.

There is general agreement that this is one of the main works of the Master of St. Severin. The picture is clearly a mature work, but whether it was done before or after the larger altarpiece of the *Adoration of the Kings* (see no.25) remains uncertain. A date around 1505–10 seems reasonable. It has been noted that the measurements of this picture—as those of the large Adoration—correspond to the Cologne ell (57,52cm).

Oak, 57× 50·5cm (1ft 9½in× 1ft 8in)
First known in the Collection of Lady Cranleigh, Grandesburgh Hall, near Norwich; then through dealers in the 1950s (and the Becker Collection, Dortmund), to the Museum in 1975.
Literature: Rolf Fritz, in: *Katalog Sammlung Becker*, I, *Gemälde alter Meister*, Dortmund 1967, no.11; Stange, no.317; Cologne Exhib., 1970, p.46f, no.30; Kurt Löcher, *Ein Altkölner Bild*, in: *Museen in Köln*, Bulletin, 14. Jg., Heft 9, Sept. 1975 p.1362.
Cologne, Wallraf-Richartz Museum, no.WRM3258.

25. The Adoration of the Kings

In the middle of the picture the Virgin and Child sit enthroned. The three kings kneel in the foreground. Behind them their servants and warriors carrying arms and standards approach from left and right. The flag on the left, showing several stars, was thought, in the Middle Ages, to be Melchior's attribute, the flag with crescent moon and star Caspar's, the flag with a Moor holding a lance Balthasar's. In the right-hand corner of the picture, St. Ursula with crown, arrow and virgins under her cloak, intercedes for the donor's wife. In the left-hand corner St. Oswald(?) with sceptre and ring intercedes for the donor. In front of the donors are the coats-of-arms of their families.

It is not quite clear whether the saint on the extreme left is St. Oswald. He may be St. Aetherius, the fiancé of St. Ursula. The attributes fit both saints. It is likely that the panel came from the church of St. Ursula where there is a splendid Aetherius shrine.

The composition of the picture is still influenced by Lochner's altarpiece in Cologne Cathedral. But more than ever before, the painter concentrates on the main subject of the Adoration in the centre. There is a slight tendency towards the grotesque. The Master does not put a monumental group in the centre; by shifting the figures of the kings and arranging them in a semicircle he avoids the danger of a rigid composition and makes the interrelations between the figures more complex.

This structural skill presupposes an experienced master. The panel is without doubt a late work and a work done by the Master himself. The donors help to date the picture; they are a married couple, the Dr art. ac utr. iur. Christian de Conreshem and his wife Hylgin, *née* Pastor. They married in 1489. The wife died presumably around 1512, for Christian Conreshem became vice-chancellor of the university for the first time in 1513 (only unmarried men were eligible). But as he is shown here without the insignia of his office it is likely that the picture was painted in 1512. This could mean that it also served as a memorial to his wife.

The altarpiece is one of the most important works of late gothic painting in Cologne.

Oak, 118 × 205cm (3ft 10½in × 6ft 8¾in). Restored 1950.
Originally from the church of St. Ursula, Cologne; later Wallraf Collection.
Literature: Stange, no.316; *Kindlers Malerei Lexikon*, v, Zürich 1968, p.438ff; J. M. Fritz, *Kölner Prunk- und Tafelsilber der Spätgotik*, in: *Festschrift für Gert von der Osten*, Cologne 1970, p.106.
Cologne, Wallraf-Richartz, no.WRM184.

The Master of St. Severin

26. Eight Female Saints

These female saints were particularly revered in Cologne. They are, from left to right: St. Ursula with arrow and crown and two accompanying virgins under her cloak; St. Gertrude of Nivelles in the robes of her Order, carrying an abbess's staff in her right hand and a book with a mouse in her left; St. Apollonia with tooth and pincers; St. Catherine with crown, broken wheel and sword; St. Barbara with tower and martyr's palm; St. Dorothea with rosary and basket of roses; St. Brigid in the robes of her Order, with cow and book; St. Cecilia crowned with roses, and holding a sword.

The group of women stand in a semicircle which largely conforms to the formal principle of the Byzantine *isokephalia*. This little picture by the Master of St. Severin clearly still observes the Cologne tradition of showing saints in a row, an arrangement faintly reminiscent of the concept of the *sacra conversazione*. Among other works, the Master's *Altarpiece of the Rosary* in St. Andreas (around 1500) and the two wings with saints in St. Severin, (shortly after 1500) are most directly comparable to this picture. The latter, in particular, shows a very similar treatment of space, draperies and facial types. There is general agreement that the painting is autograph. Its style suggests a late date, around 1510–15.

Another small picture, the *Mass of St. Gregory*, in the Wallraf-Richartz Museum (see no.27) is closely linked in technique, size and date with the picture of the eight saints.

Tempera on silk, 18·5 × 19cm (7¼in × 7½in).
First known in the collection of Dr. Kerp; then Dormagen Collection; given to the Museum in 1886.
Literature: O.H. Förster, *Das Wallraf-Richartz-Museum in Köln*, Cologne 1961, no.78; Schröder, *Dorothea (Heilige in Bild und Legende)*, Recklinghausen 1966, p.50; Stange, no.315.
Cologne, Wallraf-Richartz Museum, no.WRM187.

27. The Mass of St.
Gregory

In the centre of an ill-defined space, presumably a chapel, Pope Gregory reads the Mass. On the altar are a missal, candlesticks and a small icon. The Man of Sorrows appears in a large, bright halo. Around him are the objects of his suffering, the *arma Christi*: the column of the flagellation with rod and scourge; the cock of Peter's denial, nails, hammer, pots of ointment, the head and purse of Judas; Peter's sword with the ear of Malchus, the heads of the judges and those of the soldiers. Other fathers of the Church and holy bishops are grouped in a semi-circle, kneeling and listening. From left to right they are: St. Augustine with the heart; St. Jerome (as a father of the Church in a cardinal's robe and mitre) with the lion; St. Maximinus, bishop of Trier, in pontifical robes with crozier and bear; St. Martin as a bishop in pontifical robes with crozier, a coin in his right hand and a beggar near him; St. Ambrose, also in pontifical dress with a crozier.

For the subject, see Index of Saints: Gregory. The subject as it is shown here became extremely popular in Cologne towards the end of the century. The Wallraf-Richartz Museum has, for instance, panels of the same subject by the Master of St. Bartholomew (Dep.211) and the Master of the Holy Kindred (WRM167). The format of the picture, its miniature-like composition and its theme all suggest that it originally served as a burse cover.

There is general agreement that the picture is a work of the master's own hand. It is closely related to the picture of eight female saints (see no.26) which is of the same size. They are both mature works and were presumably done around 1510–15.

Tempera on silk, 19·4 × 19·4cm (7½in × 7½in).
Collection Essingh, Cologne; then Dr. Paul Silverberg, Lugano; given to the Museum in 1950.
Literature: H. L. Keller, *Reclams Lexikon der Heiligen und der biblischen Gestalten*, Stuttgart 1968, p.236; Stange, no.315.
Cologne, Wallraf-Richartz Museum, no.WRM868.

The Master of St.
Severin (Workshop?)

28. The Last Judgement   Christ is enthroned on a double rainbow above an open, hilly, rocky landscape. Sword and lily extend from his head. He shows the stigmata, right hand raised, left hand lowered against the damned. Beside him are two angels blowing the trumpets of doom. On the ground the dead can be seen rising from their graves. The Virgin kneels in the left foreground, praying and looking upwards; opposite her is St. John the Evangelist. On the extreme left the redeemed can be seen entering paradise through the portals of heaven; on the extreme right devils drive the damned into hell.

The panel follows Cologne tradition in presenting this subject as it had already been formulated by a Cologne master around 1410–20 (see no. 5), and by Lochner. Certain details, for instance in the right-hand group of the damned, are very close to an altarpiece wing from Weiler (Diocesan Museum, Cologne) by the Master of St. Ursula. In fact, the composition of the group and also other individual figures seem to have been taken over directly from that panel. But it has been noted that the liveliness and narrative breadth of the Weiler panel has turned brittle and dry. None the less, the drawing of the *Last Judgement* is sharp and clear, and the sculptural effect of draperies, figures and buildings is emphasised. Tröscher (1939) connected the picture with the 'taiffelgin mit dem lesten urdele' (the small panel of the Last Judgement) in the *Samstagsrentkammer* of the Cologne Town Hall, which was mentioned in 1488. Stange thought the picture a workshop piece.

Oak, 145·7 × 166·5 cm (4ft 9½ in × 5ft 5½ in). Restored in 1954.
From the Weyer Collection, Cologne; presented to the Museum in 1829.
Literature: Stange, no. 324.
Cologne, Wallraf-Richartz Museum, no. WRM183.

Cologne (?) School

*c.*1500

29. A Woman

The sitter holds prayer beads. She is shown before a wall, perhaps a window-ledge, on which are displayed an apple and a beaker of flowers. The beaker is of a type common in the Rhineland around 1500. The cloth behind the sitter seems to have been surmounted by a canopy, part of which is still visible despite the trimming of the top of the picture.

Canopies of this type are unusual in portraits, but not unknown (see no.33). They are common in religious paintings. Because of this, it has been suggested that the picture once formed part of a diptych or triptych with the lady addressing herself to the Virgin and Child. But she does not hold her hands in the attitude of prayer, and it seems more likely that the picture is an early example of the independent portrait in the Rhineland, although the *genre* was well developed elsewhere. In this case, the canopy would present visual proof of the emergence of the independent portrait from its origins in religious work.

The apple would seem to refer to Eve, and by extension to the sin of all women. Scholars have not always been in full agreement about the attribution. Originally thought to be Flemish, it became 'French School' in 1902, 'Ecole de Jean Fouquet, vers 1460' in 1904, 'German School' in 1929. Levey ascribed the painting to the Cologne School, but the sharp, bright colour, vigorous handling and interest in still-life may suggest a connection with the Westphalian workshop of Derick Baegert, and some caution over the attribution to Cologne might be wise.

Oak, painted surface, 38·4 × 28·5cm (1ft 3⅛in × 11¼in); the top is trimmed, the bottom edge minimally so. Cleaned in 1957.
First mentioned in the collection of Léon de Somzée, Brussels; acquired in 1902 by George Salting by whom bequeathed to the National Gallery in 1910.
Literature: Levey, p.17.
London, National Gallery, no.2670.

**The Master of the
Saint Bartholomew
Altarpiece**
(active in the late 15th/
early 16th century)

This anonymous artist is known as a painter and also as an illuminator of manuscripts. He is named from an altarpiece formerly in the church of St. Columba, Cologne (now Munich, Alte Pinakothek nos. 11863/4/5, but see no.30 below).

It is now generally agreed that he trained in the Netherlands and it is postulated that he moved from a first base in Gelderland to Utrecht before travelling up the Rhine to Cologne. Two altarpieces at Cologne were commissioned from him for the Carthusian monastery there, which has suggested to some scholars that the Master was himself a monk.

The Master was the most individual Cologne painter of his time. In his work piety and refinement are mingled with contorted poses and an excited linearity. He has been described as a 'Late Gothic Mannerist'.

Some of the Master's work may date from as early as 1470; some of it is as late as *c*.1510.

A *Book of Hours* (see no.31) has one miniature dated 1475.

30. Saints Peter and
Dorothea

Reverse: St. John the Evangelist and the Virgin and Child (not by the hand of the Master).

St. Peter holds two large keys (for the gates of heaven) and a book; in his left hand a pair of spectacles. St. Dorothea is crowned with a garland of small roses; she also carries a basket of them (see Index of Saints: Dorothea). St. John the Evangelist carries his serpent-filled chalice (see no.11). The Virgin holds a fig. Like the apple, the fig alludes to the Fall of Man, and would here refer specifically to Christ's future role as redeemer.

The National Gallery wing is clearly from the same altarpiece as a panel in Mainz (Mittelrheinisches Landesmuseum), unfortunately unable to travel to this exhibition because of its fragility. The Mainz panel shows *Saints Andrew and Columba*, by the Master; and, on the reverse, *Two Magi* in attitudes of adoration. Levey stated that the two pictures formed wings to an altarpiece, the saints being on the inside. Thus, when shut, the two Magi would have adored the Virgin and Child. It is difficult, however, to see how the necessary third Magus could have been inserted; also the Virgin is not in the seated attitude normal to her when in conjunction with the Magi. Goldberg and Scheffler rejected a suggestion (made in the 19th century) that the London and Mainz panels formed part of the Altarpiece of St. Bartholomew itself, even though the former are of the same height and width as the wings thereof. Most significant, they failed to remark that the thickness of the *central* panel is 1·6cm while all the other panels measure only 0·8cm at their thickest point. Thus it is legitimate to accept this as proof that the London and Mainz panels originally formed the outsides of the wings of the St. Bartholomew altar. Undoubtedly, they were cut off, at a later date, and had their reverses planed and painted with the Virgin and Child, St. John, and the two Magi. These pastiche the Cologne School style of the time, but do not conform to the standard iconography of the era. The figure of St. John the Evangelist is obviously derived from the image of the same saint in the Munich wing.

This hypothesis is given extra credence by virtue of the fact that *all* the panels

30. *Continued*

are known to have been in the church of St. Columba; indeed the Mainz wing shows St. Columba herself.

The London wing is recognised by modern scholars as a late work of the Master, perhaps of around 1505–10. Goldberg and Scheffler accept a dating after two altarpieces of 1481–1501; they point out that it inspired some parts of a painting by the Master of the Holy Company (which is no earlier than 1503).

Oak, painted surface, 1·255 × 71cm (4ft 1¼in × 2ft 3½in). Cleaned 1972; in excellent condition.
The National Gallery painting was still in the church of St. Columba in 1671; but evidently valued separately from its companion pieces in 1688. Bought, in 1815, by Prince Ludwig Kraft Ernst von Oettingen-Wallerstein from Count Joseph von Rechberg. Probably earlier in the Boisserée Collection. Then as for no.11.
Literature: Levey, p.91; Manchester Exhib., 1961, no.32; Stange, no.256; Goldberg and Scheffler, pp.231–243.
London, National Gallery, no.707.

31. Book of Hours of
Sophia of Bylant

The book has 181 parchment leaves and a 15th-century binding with various
blind stamps in lozenge-shaped fields. The calendar of saints is that of the
Utrecht diocese which was a subsidiary diocese of Cologne. The initials with
foliage and flowers are red, blue and gold. The decorated borders are filled with
intertwined tendrils and flowers. Thirteen full-page miniatures are set into the
twenty-one quires.

1. *Christ before Pilate*. Pontius Pilate sits enthroned in front of a brocade curtain in
a barrel-vaulted room. The border decoration represents an animal fable which
refers back to the main scene: animals bring a lamb before their king, the lion.
A scroll in the right-hand margin carries the inscription: *Nichil tibi de hoc iusto*
(Matthew XXVI,19).

2. *The Tree of Jesse*. A tree grows out of the patriarch Jesse; in its branches sit
twelve kings of the Old Testament who are the ancestors of Christ (Isaiah XI,1).
The two uppermost kings kneel in adoration before the Virgin and Child in the
crown of the tree. The animals in the border, eagle, pelican, ram and unicorn are
symbols for Christ and also refer back to the Old Testament scene in the centre.

3. *The Presentation of the Virgin*: Mary is led by an angel up a long flight of steps to
the temple. To the left of the stair is Mary's father Joachim, together with two
other men; to the right her mother Anne with a servant. The border shows Christ
as a small child. A putto (at the bottom) carries the Dorenwerth coat-of-arms,
representing the estate which the patron inherited from her first husband. Below
this is the 18th-century inscription 'Dorenweerdt'.

4. *The Annunciation*. God the Father can be seen in heaven, surrounded by a host
of angels, sending the Christ Child with the cross down to Mary.

5. *The Flagellation*. On the tiled floor at the front is the date MCCCCLXXV. In the
lower border a honey-sucking bear is attacked by bees. The scroll belonging to
this scene says: '*An den honich hed ick gevonden Den smaeck lieten mi die bie mit
gewaer*' (I would like the honey if only the bees would let me). A scroll in the
left border says: '*Och muuch ich in vreden zijn*' (O that I were at peace).

6. *The Crowning with Thorns*. Pilate is seen at the right-hand edge of the picture;
spectators watch the event through a window on the left. The border is decorated
with animals and fabulous creatures: an eagle who has killed a lamb, a centaur
with an abducted child, a fox with a hen in his mouth, an owl, a marten sucking a
hen's egg, a bird of prey with a smaller bird. All these make symbolic reference to
the picture in the centre.

31. *Continued*

7. *Christ carrying the Cross.* Christ's robe is weighed down by a block of wood to increase his suffering. Soldiers drive him forward while on the left Simon of Cyrene helps him to carry the cross. The Virgin and St. John are at the left edge of the picture.

8. *The Crucifixion.* The Virgin and St. John mourn beside the cross. The background is of gilt repoussé work. The borders are decorated with foliage and flowers, and birds of paradise.

9. *St. John the Baptist with Reynalt von Homoet.* To the right of the saint, and smaller than he, kneels Reynalt von Homoet, owner of Dorenwerth, husband of the lady who commissioned the book; he is dressed in fashionable clothes. Above him is his coat-of-arms. A scroll around the head of St. John the Baptist bears the inscription: '*Ecce agnus dei ecce qui tollit peccata mundi*'. Among the foliage, flowers and birds of paradise of the border two angels can be seen, one praying, one playing a musical instrument. Underneath the border is the later inscription 'Homoet'.

10. *The Apostle James the Great with Sophia von Bylant.* To the right of the Saint kneels Sophia von Byland in prayer; she wears fashionable Burgundian dress. Above her is her coat-of-arms. The halo of the saint is inscribed '*Santus iacobus maior*'. The border is decorated with intertwined tendrils and flowers, and subsidiary coats-of arms.

11. *The Adoration.* Joseph sits behind the Virgin and Child, with the ox and the ass beside him. Zelomi and Salome, the two nurses, approach from the left. In the background to the right the annunciation to the shepherds can be seen.

12. *The Funeral Mass.* The cloth of the catafalque bears the coat-of-arms of Sophia von Bylant. The lower border has a skull and a scroll inscribed '*Miseremini mei mei miseremini mei saltem vos amisi mei*' (Job XIX,21).

13. *The Adoration of the Three Kings.* The Virgin and Child sit inside a ruin with a thatched roof in an open landscape. The Three Kings approach from the right to offer their gifts. The first king has sunk to his knees, adoring Christ. The borders are decorated with intertwined tendrils, flowers and birds of paradise.

31. *Continued*

The coats-of-arms of the pictures including the donors show that the manuscript was commissioned by Sophia von Bylant. She and her husband, Reynalt von Homoet, came from noble Guelders families. Reynalt died as early as 1458/9 and Sophia is therefore assumed to have been the sole patron who made the painter include a posthumous portrait of her husband as a memento. The picture of the funeral mass with Sophia's coat-of arms has to be interpreted as a *memento mori*. Sophia died in 1498; miniature no.5 however is dated 1475 – thus the funeral mass can not be connected with Sophia's own death. The Utrecht calendar of saints seems to make it probable that the manuscript originated in this town, but other aspects (mainly stylistic and linguistic ones) point to Arnhem as the place of origin. Apart from miniature no.13 all pictures can be assumed to have been done by the Master of St. Bartholomew himself. Their quality varies, however, and one can construct a chronological sequence which starts with the miniature showing the *Virgin in the Temple*.

Parchment, 181 leaves in 21 quires; 23·2 × 16·5cm (9⅛ × 6½in). The miniatures vary in size; smallest 11·4 × 9·3cm (4½ × 3⅝in) (min.no.11), largest 20·3 × 14·7cm (8 × 5¾in) (min.no.10). On the fly-leaf in gothic writing: 'Dit boeck hoert toe Marie van homoet, vedue van Montfoert'. Maria of Homoet was Sophia's daughter.
1959, acquired by the museum.
Literature: Cologne Exhib., 1961, p.13ff and 21ff, and no.9; Cologne Exhib., 1970, no.105; Paul Pieper, *Miniaturen des Bartholomäus-Meisters*, in: *Wallraf-Richartz-Jahrbuch*, XV, 1953, p.135ff; Paul Pieper, *Das Stundenbuch des Bartholomäus-Meisters*, in: *Wallraf-Richartz-Jahrbuch*, XXI, 1959, p.97ff.
Cologne, Wallraf-Richartz Museum, nos.M232–244.

32. The Journey of the
Three Kings
Reverse:
The Assumption of the
Virgin

The three Magi appear twice (see Index of Saints: Three Magi). In the background, they appear in the role of astronomers. Perched on high mountains they look upwards at the sky. Originally the star of Bethlehem would have been visible there, but the top of the panel has been cut away.

In the foreground, they are shown in the role of pilgrims. They meet in a clearing, each accompanied by a standard bearer as well as by other attendants.

The version of the story shown is that perpetuated by Johannes von Hildesheim (published early 16th century, but written earlier), and in the *Golden Legend* (a book comprising the Lives of the Saints compiled in the 13th century). In the left corner is David, who carries a scroll bearing the Latin version of Psalms ch. LXXII,10 ('*The kings of Tarshish and of the isles shall bring presents: the kings of Sheba and Seba shall offer gifts*'). In the right corner, Isaiah carries a scroll with an inscription identified as *Ysaie LX°* (actually, Isaiah ch. LX,14: '*All they that despised thee shall bow themselves down at the soles of thy feet*'). Both of these Old Testament passages were held to prophesy the Adoration of the Magi.

Reverse: God the Father awaits the arrival of the Virgin, a crown in his hands ready to effect her coronation as Queen of Heaven.

There has been some discussion of the reconstruction first proposed in the Manchester Exhibition of 1960. Despite certain discrepancies in the sizes, it is quite acceptable.

It is clear that this panel, painted on both sides, is part of an altarpiece-wing. The reconstruction places the *Journey of the Magi* above an *Adoration of the Magi* (Munich, Alte Pinakothek, no.10651); on the reverse, the *Assumption* would have surmounted the *Dormition of the Virgin* (now destroyed, formerly in Berlin). The composition of the rest of the altarpiece is unknown, save that a *Nativity* (Paris, Petit Palais) probably occupied part of the other wing.

Generally accepted as being an early work, painted by the Master, when he was still in Holland, i.e. before *c*.1480.

Oak, 61·6 × 69·8cm (2ft ½in × 2ft 3½in). Cut at each edge.
Acquired by Henry Blundell between 1803 and 1810; then by descent to the present owner.
Literature: Manchester Exhib., *Works of Art from Private Collections*, 1960, no.19; Cologne Exhib., 1961, no.10; Manchester Exhib., 1961, no.34; Stange, no.238; Goldberg & Scheffler, pp.226–231; Paris Exhib., *Les Primitifs de l'Ecole de Cologne*, 1974, no.11.
Private Collection.

33. Portrait of a Man

The sitter holds a columbine in his right hand.

The sitter's name is not known to us; his dress suggests that he is a middle-class burgher. The church tower is in all probability the tower of Utrecht cathedral. Some scholars have thought that the picture was painted in Cologne and that the sitter might be a former Utrecht citizen, who had consciously chosen the view through the window as a reminder of his origin. It has also been suggested that the sitter might be Reynalt von Homoet who died in 1458 or 1459 (which would make this picture a posthumous portrait); he had been the husband of Sophia von Bylant for whom the Master of St. Bartholomew painted a marvellous Book of Hours in 1475, now in the Wallraf-Richartz Museum (see no.31). In any case the connection with Utrecht is obvious and confirms that the master's own artistic origins were in Guelders/Utrecht, from where he continued to receive commissions.

The original frame of the panel is lost and we do not know whether it was the right wing of a diptych; the left wing might have shown the Virgin. The way the sitter turns to the left, and also the presence of the columbine (symbol of Christ and also of melancholia) favour such an interpretation. The interesting motif of the brocade curtain held up by angels could have been used because a similar curtain framed the figure of the Virgin in the corresponding panel. Scholars are agreed that the master himself painted this picture, because the portrait is so distinctive, and because of its draughtsmanship and painting technique as well as its striking colours. It is thought to have been done around 1480–5.

Oak, 32·5 × 22·5cm (1ft ¾in × 8⅞in). Restored in 1965. The panel is slightly cut down at the bottom below the stone parapet.
From the collection of The Princess Royal (sold 1924); acquired for the Museum in 1965.
Literature: Ernst Buchner, *Das deutsche Bildnis der Spätgotik und der frühen Dürerzeit,* Berlin 1953, p.35, no.15, fig.15; Paul Pieper, *Miniaturen des Bartholomäus-Meisters,* in: *Wallraf-Richartz-Jahrbuch,* XV, 1953, p.150f; Rolf Wallrath, *Bildnis eines Unbekannten vom Meister des Bartholomäusalters,* in: *Wallraf-Richartz-Jahrbuch,* XXVII, 1965, p.389ff, fig.268; Gert von der Osten, *Ein Bildnis des Bartholomäus-Meisters,* in: *Museen in Köln, Bulletin,* 4. Jg. Heft 12, Dez. 1965, p.426f; Stange, no.259; Cologne Exhib., 1970, no.33.
Cologne, Wallraf-Richartz Museum, no.WRM882.

The Master of the Saint Bartholomew Altarpiece

34. Fragment of an Altarpiece (head of a young man)

This head of a young man has clearly been cut from a larger panel. Other small fragments by the hand of the master have been said to have formed part of the same altarpiece. One head (not in the exhibition, but illustrated opposite) certainly belongs. It is said to be that of St. James the Great, but is perhaps only that of a pilgrim.

It has been said that the fragments formed part of a central panel to which the London and Mainz panels formed wings. This is unacceptable as now demonstrated in the entry to no.30. The fragments are usually dated late (*c.*1500–1510), but now seem more likely to be in the Master's earlier style.

Oak, 14·6 × 13·2cm ($5\frac{3}{4} \times 5\frac{1}{4}$in). In the collection of Sir Robert Witt, London, in 1952. Bequeathed by him to the Courtauld Institute.
Literature: Cologne Exhib., 1961, no.26; Manchester Exhib., 1961, no.19; Stange, no.258.
London, Courtauld Institute of Art, Sir Robert Witt Collection.

The Master of the Saint Bartholomew Altarpiece

35. The Virgin and Child with Musical Angels

Above the Virgin's head four angels sing in tune to the music made by the others. They read their words from a scroll which is inscribed *regina celi letare* (O Queen of Heaven, rejoice). On the left grows a columbine; on the right in a vase are Sweet William.

Both flowers are Christian symbols. The Columbine was so-called because of its appearance (i.e. 'like a dove') and therefore alludes to the Holy Ghost. It generally has seven blooms, which therefore conveniently refer to the Seven Gifts of the Holy Spirit.

Generally thought to have been painted at some time between 1480 and 1495; the earlier part of that span might now seem more correct. Obviously created as a panel for private devotion.

Oak, 52 × 38cm (1ft 7½in × 1ft 3in), round top. In the Ralph Bernal Sale (Christies, 1855). *Literature:* Cologne Exhib., 1961, no.21; Manchester Exhib., 1961, no.33; Stange, no.249. Private Collection.

36. The Deposition

The action is conceived as taking place within a carved shrine, rather as if the painting were part of a sculptural altar. The body of Christ is received at the bottom of the ladder by Joseph of Arimathaea; on the ladder is Nicodemus and, at the top, an unidentified helper. The Virgin swoons in the arms of St. John the Evangelist. The Magdalen, on right, holds her head and seems to lean on the ladder for support. At the top of the cross are visible the Hebrew and Greek versions of the more usual Latin *Jesus Nazarenus Rex Judorum*. One of the most dramatic works of the Master, it compares most directly with a large *Deposition* (Paris, Louvre no.1445), whose recent cleaning shows it to be a late work *c.*1501/1505. This *Deposition* could well be contemporaneous.

Oak, 74·9 × 47·3cm (2ft 6in × 4ft 6¾in).
First mentioned in 1714 as the property of the Ingram family at Temple Newsam; then by descent to the present owner.
Literature: Cologne Exhib., 1961, no.24; Manchester Exhib., 1961, no.29; Stange, no.247.
The Earl of Halifax, Garrowby.

37. The Altarpiece of
the Crucifixion
See frontispiece

The central panel of this triptych shows the crucified Christ. Mourning angels surround him. The Virgin and St. John stand beneath the cross; their gestures express their extreme anguish. Beside the Virgin is the Father of the Church, Jerome, in the robes and hat of a cardinal, in front of him his attribute, the lion. Beside St. John is Thomas, the apostle, reading a book and carrying his attribute, the carpenter's square. The Magdalen kneels at the foot of the cross and embraces it in despair. In front of her are a skull, bones and the pot of ointment.

The inner side of the left wing shows St. John the Baptist with the lamb and St. Cecilia with a portative organ held up in a sling by an angel.

On the inner side of the right wing are the two corresponding figures of St. Alexius, with pilgrim's clothes and hat and a scroll, and St. Agnes, reading a book. St. Agnes carries the palm of martyrdom; a lamb is at her feet (see Index of Saints).

When the altarpiece is closed, the outer sides of the wings show the *Annunciation* in the lower part. Intertwined tendrils separate this scene from the upper part where the crouching figure of St. Peter can be seen on the left; St. Paul to the right.

The panels are distinguished by strongly realistic figures and scenes. The figures are very sculptural. This is particularly evident in the grisaille paintings of the outer wings, where the figures in the *Annunciation* almost look like sculptures. And the painting of the centre panel suggests a carved altarpiece, thus also reflecting this new, more realistic attitude.

It has never been doubted that the Master himself painted all parts of this altarpiece. Several aspects suggest that the altarpiece is a late work of the Master. The figure of St. Thomas for instance can be compared with the St. Peter in London (see no.30). The sources, too, suggest a later date than 1480-90. Dr jur. utriusque Peter Rink (d.1501) left the panels to the Carthusian monastery, one of the most important in Cologne, in his will dated 5 May 1500. The altar would thus have been painted around the year 1500.

Centre Panel: 107×80cm (3ft 6in×2ft 7½in); Wings: 107×34cm (3ft 6in×1ft 1½in) each. On the cross of the centre panel: IS NAZARENUS RE (x). On Jerome's book: SVME ANTONINI. On the frame of the left inner wing: SCS IOHANES: BAPTISTA SCA: CEILIA: VIRGO. On the right inner wing: SCS ALEXCIVS: SCA AGNES: VIRGO. On the archangel Gabriel's scroll (left outer wing): AV(e).GRACIA. PLENA. DOMINUS T. On the scroll of the right outer wing: ECCE. ANCILLA. (do)MINI. FIAT. MIHI. SECUNDU(m). (verbum.T)VVM. Restored in 1949.
From the Corthusian Monastery, Cologne; Lyvesberg collection, Cologne (sold 1837); collection of Freiherr von Geyr, Cologne; acquired for the Museum in 1862, with the Richartz Fund.
Literature: Cologne Exhib., 1961, no.25; Stange, no.254; Günter Busch, *Ein bisher unerkanntes Werk des Bartholomäus-Meisters*, in: *Festschrift für Gert von der Osten*, Köln 1970, p.126ff,127, fig.8.
Cologne, Wallraf-Richartz Museum, no.WRM180.

38. The Madonna with
the Walnut

The Virgin's right breast is exposed and her robe falls over a stone parapet; on
this parapet lies a walnut.

The Madonna's exposed breast refers back to the 'Maria lactans' motif (see
no.46). Most of the details are symbolic. The brocade curtain is reminiscent of the
gilt background of earlier panels, yet at the same time acts as a halo. The arch and
tendrils above are a formal device closing off the picture, but they also emphasise
the majesty of the madonna. The precious stones in her golden crown and in the
tendrils refer to the Queen of Heaven and to Christ. The two female figures in
the landscape on the right may be the two Holy Women, Mary and Elisabeth.
The walnut has a symbolic relevance for both the Madonna and Christ. Contemporary sermons refer to the Mother of the Lord as a tree which 'produced the
nuts of all virtue and sweetness'. Augustine compared the nut itself with Christ.
Its green outer skin symbolises Christ's Passion, its kernel divine redemption, the
hard shell the wood of the cross. It is also possible that the nut refers symbolically
to the virginity of the Madonna.

It has never been doubted that the Master of St. Bartholomew himself painted
this panel. But its date has been disputed. But it now seems certain that the little
panel belongs to the Master's late period, that is 1500–1510.

Oak, 30 × 20·3cm (11¾ × 8in). Last restored in 1950.
Collection Dr. Franz Jos. Kerp (d.1841), Köln; collection Dr Hubert Dormagen, 1886,
bequeathed to the Wallraf-Richartz Museum.
Literature: Cologne Exhib., 1961, no.28; Paul Pieper, *Miniaturen des Bartholomäus-Meisters,
Wallraf-Richartz-Jahrbuch,* in: XV, 1953, p.152f; Ernst Buchner, *Das deutsche Bildnis der
Spätgotik und der frühen Dürerzeit,* Berlin 1953, p.33, no.12; Stange, no.246; Günter Busch,
Ein bisher unerkanntes Werk des Bartholomäus-Meisters, in: *Festschrift für Gert von der Osten,*
Köln, 1970, p.126, abb.7.
Cologne, Wallraf-Richartz Museum, no.WRM578.

The Master of the Aachen Altarpiece
(active in the late 15th/ early 16th century)

This anonymous painter is named after a large triptych now in the treasury of Aachen Cathedral, but originally painted for the church of the Carmelites in Cologne. Recently there have been attempts to identify him with, on the one hand, 'Hermann Soytmann' (documented as a goldsmith), and with a printmaker (the Master PW). Neither identification has found general acceptance.

The style of the Master has clear connections with those of his contemporaries, the Masters of the Ursula Legend and of St. Severin. His activity is presumed to span the period from around 1495 to about 1525.

His distinguishing characteristics include exaggerated physical expression, caricatured heads and compositions based on a turmoil of moving figures, many of whom wear fantastic eastern costumes.

39. The Crucifixion

Christ is shown on the cross between the two thieves. The legs of the latter have been broken to facilitate death by suffocation, thereby cutting short their suffering; Christ was not treated with such savage kindness. In the background left, Christ falls beneath the cross; on the right, *The Deposition*. The Virgin and St. John the Evangelist stand by the foot of the cross. On the left, three holy women mourn; on the right, soldiers play dice for Christ's robe.

The edges of the Virgin's robe are inscribed STABAT MATRE (for STABAT MATER known, during the 15th century, as a hymn). Around her head is the inscription QUIS. (E)ST. HOM/VI.NON.FLE/MATREM. CRISTI. S(I?)VI(D)/IN.TANTO.SU(P) (= Who is the man who would not weep seeing the Mother of Christ in such distress).

The painting was found to be the central panel of a triptych, the wings of which are in Liverpool (Walker Art Gallery, nos.1225/6; unfortunately not loaned to the exhibition, but illustrated opposite). For some time the National Gallery painting has been united with its wings; the latter show *Christ before Pilate* and *The Lamentation*. When the reverses of the wings were cleaned, they were discovered to be painted by the hand of the Master; they show *The Mass of St. Gregory* and *Two Donors*. When the triptych is closed the donors are seen to be in the church in which the mass is being celebrated. The donors are identified by their coats-of-arms as Hermann Rinck (Mayor of Cologne in 1480 and 1488) and his wife Gertrud von Dallem. Rinck died on 12 March 1496. *The Pilate* wing depends on a panel by Derick Baegert (Brussels, Musées Royaux des Beaux-Arts no.4916), which cannot be earlier than 1489. This provides a broad dating of 1489–1496 for the altar.

Oak, painted area, 107·3 × 120·3cm (3ft 6¼in × 3ft 11⅜in). Cleaned 1962–64.
Recorded as being brought from Flanders to England at the time of the French Revolution. Presented by Edward Shipperdson, 1847.
Literature: Levey, p.63; Cologne Exhib., 1961, no.40A; Manchester Exhib. 1961, no.60; Walker Art Gallery: *Foreign Schools Catalogue,* 1963, p.104; J. Jacob, *The Master of the Aachen Altarpiece: a Discovery* in *The Liverpool Bulletin,* vol.11, 1963–6, p.7; Stange, no.333. London, National Gallery, no.1049.

40. Inventories of the
Windeck Guild

The two miniatures show the *Virgin and Child* and a *Bishop making the Sign of Benediction*. The Virgin is shown as the Queen of Heaven and sits on a pinnacled throne, holding a flower (rose?) in her right hand and holding up the standing Christ Child with her left hand. He has a halo with an inscribed cross. In the foreground kneel members of the guild. In the second miniature a bishop stands on a narrow strip of ground. He may be St. Nicholas, the patron saint of sailors. Below him two further members of the guild (merchants?) pray. The two miniatures are on a double page (1 *verso* and 2 *recto*) which serve as the frontispiece to a volume containing inventories of the Windeck guild covering the years 1546–1736. The miniatures are much earlier and must therefore have been taken from an earlier manuscript and added to this inventory. But the figures of the donors suggest that the miniatures were originally used in a very similar context. The 'Gaffeln', or new guilds, began in 1396 and arose out of mergers of the older guilds whose main functions they took over. There were 22 'Gaffeln' and from 1396 onwards they provided 36 of the 49 members of the new city council. The Windeck 'Gaffel' was one of the most important Cologne guilds, since it represented the table company of merchants on the *Altermarkt* who traded mainly with England. The close trade relations between Cologne and England go back to the 12th century and continued later when Cologne was a member of the Hansa. This is thought to be why the two miniatures (and the paintings in the choir of Cologne Cathedral) show English influence. The psalter of Robert de Lisle in London (Brit. Mus., Arundel 83 II) has been mentioned in this context.

Parchment, 56 sheets, embossed leather binding with clasps, 17·8 × 12·8cm (7in × 5in).
Literature: Exhib. cat., *England und Köln*, Cologne 1965, p.18ff; Exhib. cat., *Kölner archivalische Kostbarkeiten*, Cologne 1971, p.38f, no.69, fig.14; Cologne Exhib., 1974, no.75. Cologne, Historisches Archiv, Zunftakten no.75.

41. Book on which Oaths were taken, belonging to the Guild Council

The Virgin stands to the left of the cross. To the right stands St. John. Quatrefoils in the corners contain the symbols of the evangelists; a quatrefoil on either side contains the Cologne coat-of-arms.

This miniature of the *Crucifixion* is on the back of a double quire (2 *verso*) which is otherwise blank. The end-paper with the *Crucifixion* served as a page on which the city's servants (and presumably also its councillors) had to take their oaths. The book is a document of Cologne democracy. The town's guilds rebelled against the patricians in 1396 (after a first, unsuccessful rising by the weavers in 1370) and took over the government of the town. The new constitution was laid down on 18 June 1396. It has been noted that the style of this miniature is close to that of the *Klarenaltar* (from the convent of St. Clare, now in Cologne Cathedral, 1360–70); but the figures are already bulkier and the outlines fuller and softer (Zehnder). Colour gradations and white highlights replace the linear style which predominated in the earlier painting. The page differs from the other sheets in the book in size, type of parchment and colouring. It may therefore be that the first double quire, together with another end-paper, was added later. It is also strange that the sheet is not at all worn—as pages in other books on which oaths were taken often are. Perhaps the sheet had been taken out of another manuscript, or was a new version of an earlier, possibly worn-down original. The town's 1372 book for oaths (*Histor. Archiv*, Verf. und Verw. v.4) has been mentioned as a possible source (Zehnder).

Parchment, 70 sheets, Renaissance binding, 34×23·5cm (1ft 1⅜in×9¼in).
Literature: P. Fuchs, *Köln*, Cologne 1968, fig.117; Exhib. cat., *Kölner archivalische Kostbarkeiten*, Cologne 1971, p.26, no.42, fig.9; Zehnder, 1973, p.78ff; Cologne Exhib., 1974, no.82.
Cologne, Historisches Archiv, Verf. and Verw. no.v.8.

42. The Crucifixion with
the Virgin and St. John

This *Crucifixion* is of a type popular in Cologne around and after 1400. Christ's
body is straight, the two figures on either side mourn reticently. While the
figure of the suffering Christ is dramatized, the Virgin and St. John express their
grief in quiet gestures. The miniature has all the marks of International Gothic
which was first introduced into Cologne shortly before 1400. The pictures of
the Master of St. Veronica in particular, served as prototypes for such crucifixions. Yet the figure of Christ and its pose seem to reflect Westphalian models.
The softly flowing draperies and calm gestures, as well as certain details, such
like the head of Christ and the position of the Virgin's crossed hands (which
symbolize the Passion), are frequently found in Cologne panel paintings of
around 1400 (see nos. 1 and 41). Details like the plinth-like figure of the Virgin and
framing-device are widespread in Cologne. It remains uncertain whether this
miniature was a page of a missal or of a book on which oaths were taken.

Body-colour on parchment, 21·3 × 14·3cm (8⅜in × 5⅝in).
Acquired 1926.
Literature: Exhib. cat., *Handzeichnungen des 15. und 16. Jahrh. und Miniaturen aus den Samm-
lungen des Wallraf-Richartz-Museums*, Cologne 1965, no.76.
Cologne, Wallraf-Richartz Museum, no.M79.

43. Leaf from a Gradual showing the *Resurrection*

The scene is shown within the initial R, which is, in turn, enclosed in a square. Christ carries the triumphal banner.

The leaf belongs to a gradual (i.e. a book containing the chants for the mass). The composition of the scene follows the arrangement typical of Cologne around 1400, and recorded in countless examples. Yet this miniature is particularly close to a scene by the Master of St. Lawrence (see nos.8,10) in the diagonal disposition of the sarcophagus, general spatial arrangement, placing of soldiers and characterisation of Christ. Yet the correspondences with a *Resurrection* miniature in another Book of Hours (Musée Calvet, Avignon) of about 1415, show both to be by the same master, who must have worked very close to the Master of St. Lawrence himself.

Body-colour and gold on parchment. Leaf, 56 × 40·4cm (1ft 10in × 1ft 4in), miniature 15·2 × 14·1cm (6in × 5½in).
Literature: H. Jerchel, *Die Niederrheinische Buchmalerei der Spätgotik* (1380–1470), in: *Wallraf-Richartz-Jahrbuch*, x, 1938, p.65ff, no.24.
Cologne, Wallraf-Richartz Museum, no.m222.

The Master of the Lyversberg Passion
(active from about 1460 to 1490)

This anonymous painter is named from two panels, showing scenes from the Passion, which were, around 1800, in the collection of Jakob Johann Lyversberg in Cologne.

He is generally thought to have been a partner in the workshop of the Master of the Life of the Virgin, and his individual personality is now stressed by almost all scholars. He displays much influence from Netherlandish art.

44. The Crucifixion with the Virgin and St. John

The Virgin turns slightly away from the cross. On the other side of the cross St. John seems to look past Christ into the unknown. He holds a book under his left arm which characterizes him as the evangelist. The ground is shown to be Golgotha by the skulls and bones lying on it. The sun is seen to the left above the horizontal bar of the cross, the moon to the right.

The style of this miniature is very close to that of crucifixions by the Master of the Life of the Virgin who was the most important master in Cologne in the second half of the 15th century. The figure of Christ in particular is very similar to those on many panels by this painter. It follows a type established by Rogier van der Weyden which became the model for virtually all Cologne crucifixions done towards the end of the century. The altarpiece in Cues and a small panel in the Wallraf-Richartz Museum (WRM125) are good examples of this type. But the overall composition of our picture is even closer to the *Crucifixion* in an *Alterpiece of the Virgin* (Linz) which has been attributed to the Master of the Lyversberg Passion. The Linz altarpiece is of around 1461–3 and is more developed in style, so that the miniature was presumably done earlier. It may have been the canon table page of a missal.

Body-colour and gilt on parchment, 28·9 × 20·1cm (11⅜ × 7⅞in).
Presented by the Malmedé art firm, 1933.
Literature: A. Boeckler, *Deutsche Buchmalerei der Gotik*, Königstein 1959, fig.71; Exhib. cat., *Handzeichnungen des 15. und 16. Jahrh. und Miniaturen aus den Sammlungen des Wallraf-Richartz-Museums*, Cologne 1965, no.77; H. Schmidt, *Studien zur spätgotischen Malerei in Köln. Der Meister des Marienlebens und sein Kreis*. Diss. Bonn 1969, p.101f, cat.no.13; Cologne Exhib., 1970, no.102.
Cologne, Wallraf-Richartz Museum, no.M79a.

Flemish School, 1484

45. Hanseatic Cartulary The title-page of this cartulary is a rectangle which has been subdivided three times, both horizontally and vertically, to make nine small rectangular fields. In the centre field is the imperial coat-of-arms on a blue ground. In the field above is the emperor himself, enthroned, with sceptre, crown, imperial orb and coat-of-arms on his robe. Beside and below him in the fields from left to right are the seven electors wearing mitres or electoral hats or crowns, each with his sword and coat-of-arms. Behind the emperor and the electors are blue, green or red curtains. The centre field has an elaborate border of interlaced tendrills with animals and flowers.

The manuscript has an old binding with blind stamps and engraved clasps. It contains copies of the privileges which were granted to the German merchants of the Bruges office of the Hanseatic League up to 1457. Cologne merchants had connections with the Bruges office which was one of the most important of the League's trading-stations outside the empire. The Hansa decided in 1593 that the manuscript should be kept in Cologne. The subject of the miniature, the emperor surrounded by his seven electors, is rare in secular iconography. Cologne was an important member of the Hanseatic League and meetings were held in Cologne in 1367 in one of the most beautiful council chambers of Europe, later called the *Hansa Chamber*. Many other (text) pages in this manuscript have decorated borders. Its style is thought to be Flemish.

Parchment, 224 sheets, 32× 23cm (1ft ½in× 9in). On the engraved clasps: *Ave Maria gratia plena.*
Literature: P. Fuchs, *Köln*, Cologne 1968, fig.108; Exhib.cat., *Kölner archivalische Kostbarkeiten*, Cologne 1971, no.68.
Cologne, Historisches Archiv, Hanse no.1a.

Sculpture, Textiles and Stained Glass

Many of the panel-paintings and sculptures shown in museums and galleries today originally formed part of late gothic 'winged altarpieces'. These were large wooden retables which could be opened to reveal different panels. Churches were almost as densely packed with them as were the altarpieces themselves crowded with figures and scenes. Where old church-furnishings remain, the spectator gets some impression of how people in late gothic times took pleasure in pictures and spectacles. As vividly as in a Passion play, the joys and sorrows of the Virgin, the Passion of our Lord, the lives and martyrdoms of the saints are shown; a realistic, popular art, understood by everybody.

Sculpture, three-dimensional and tangible, suggests the real presence of holy figures and stories even more strongly than panel-painting. Figures in late gothic pictures always look as if they were painted versions of sculptures, not immaterial beings projected on to a plane, but fully-rounded, tangible people. Thus Stephan Lochner's famous *Madonna with the Violet* from St. Cecilia in Cologne (the building which now houses the Schnütgen Museum) is the largest icon of German late gothic art; but at the same time the Virgin is a 'sculpted' figure. This interrelation between painting and sculpture is characteristic of late gothic art in general. A winged altarpiece, when open, shows the saints of the central part in their physical presence; yet their colour unites them with the picture-plane again, like a planar, Byzantine iconostasis.

According to mediaeval usage such a retable is called a 'table' regardless of whether it is made up of painted panels alone, or whether it also includes sculpture. 'Imago' is the term for all representation of figures, whether painted or sculpted. Physical qualities and formal categories were not the most important criteria. All art exists in the gap between naturalism and idealism, and this is particularly true of the late gothic art of Cologne–whether it is painted or sculpted, transparent (as in a stained glass panel) 'painted' with a needle, or executed in any other technique.

The earliest sculptures shown here were made at the beginning of the 15th century, the latest works being created in the period which ends mediaeval art and begins modern art, which is marked, in Germany, by the year in which Albrecht Dürer and Mathias Grünewald died (1528). During this period, in which the middle class was most prominent, the art of sculpture flourished more than at any time before or after. Around the middle of the 15th century the stylistic characteristics of Stephan Lochner's art (which in itself has almost become a permanent characteristic of the Cologne school) are also clearly reflected in sculpture of the time. Oak and walnut are the principal materials used in Cologne sculpture of the late Middle Ages.

It has become a widely-accepted view that late gothic sculpture, whether it was made in Trier or Strasbourg or Vienna, entered a new epoch when the influence of the great sculptor Nicolaus Gerhaerts van Leyden became widespread, and that the works which reflect this influence vary very much in style. But the art of the Lower Rhine is much less diverse than South German art; it retains a much higher degree of uniformity. Dynamic vehemence, which characterizes the Upper Rhine, Bavaria and the Danube, is foreign to this art. A strong continuity of artistic development permeates the work of Cologne and the Lower Rhine. Tradition determines the style and also the figure-types; it is always quietly present in the art of Cologne.

Cologne sculpture of the decades around 1500 has only very recently been brought into focus. Its character is largely determined by the extensive workshop of Tilman van der Burch, an enterprise run almost on the lines of a modern factory where many artists were employed. His colossal figure of St. Christopher in Cologne Cathedral is like a figure from legend, a product of popular tales. Relations with patrons, workshop connections spanning large distances, the widespread influence of certain artistic centres and a large-scale trade resulted in multiple stylistic interrelations between late gothic towns. The artistic individuality of different regions became obscured. None the less Cologne sculpture remained calm, realistic and gentle, neither vehement nor physically aggressive. Its reticent, self-contained form is the Cologne idiom. And it is also characteristic that the stylistic influence of Nicolaus Gerhaerts, the great artistic pioneer of Upper Germany, is confined to single motifs and to the odd detail of a figure; there is no general acceptance of this newly-popular style.

Like the sculptures, the examples of stained-glass and textiles have been chosen because they too demonstrate the cross-currents between painting and the other visual arts. Holy figures and earthly concerns, mysteries and realities all seem to find their place in a perfect and practicable world view of Christian salvation. This world view is conserved with both clarity and purity by the late gothic panel-painters of Cologne and their fellow artists who worked in other media and belonged to other guilds.

Anton Legner

Cologne School,
About 1420

46. 'Madonna lactans'   This sculpture was created within the tradition of small gothic hardwood sculptures and statuettes made by 15th-century goldsmiths. These works were made for private devotion. The ancient image of the breast-feeding mother, the *Madonna lactans* or *Galaktotrophusa* (as she was called in Byzantine art), was much revered and widely-known. The humanist ideas of the *Devotio moderna*, which emerged at the end of the 14th century, laid the foundation for the new character of these devotional works, which are the sculptural equivalent of small paintings like the little panel of the *Virgin and Child in a Meadow* (no.4). The original colouring is lost and with it much of the charm which distinguished this delicate work of the Cologne school.

Walnut, 37cm high, freestanding. The original polychromy has completely disappeared. The right hand of the Virgin and the Child's left leg are restored.
Literature: A. Legner, *Marienandachtsbilder der Spätgotik: Die Gottesmutter, Marienbild im Rheinland und Westfalen*, Recklinghausen 1974, p.125.
Cologne, Schnütgen Museum, no. A49.

Cologne School,
about 1450

47. Angels carrying
Candlesticks

The particular characteristic of these angels, who carry fine gothic wooden candlesticks, is their naïve cheerfulness. They are related to the angels in Stephan Lochner's pictures. These little angels with their simple robes are most reminiscent of the servers in processions on Lochner's panels. Deep holes in the undersides suggest that the angels themselves were originally mounted on poles and carried in processions.

Oak, 45cm high, freestanding. 62·5cm and 61cm (2ft 0¾in and 2ft) respectively including wings. The finish is old, but damaged and restored. The left arm and candlestick of one of the angels is missing.
Literature: A. Legner, 1970, p.75, nos.1,2.
Cologne, Schnütgen Museum, no. A758a,b.

Cologne School,
about 1450/60

48. The Virgin and
Child with St. Anne

The Virgin's mother, of youthful yet matronly appearance, is enthroned on a
wide seat; on her lap sits a very youthful Mother of Christ; she in turn holds the
Christ Child on her lap; he raises his hand in benediction. All three figures are
quiet and gentle. The *Sedes sapientiae* has been enlarged to include an extra
generation. The 15th and 16th centuries saw great iconographical variety in
the representation of the *Virgin and Child with St. Anne*; the cult of St. Anne
was at its height. This type of group, the tiny figures of the Virgin and Child
almost taking on the character of St. Anne's attributes, follows a well-established
tradition. The style of the carving and the raised colour of this charming little
devotional group still belong to the period principally represented by Stephan
Lochner.

Walnut, height 30·5cm (1ft), freestanding. Original finish partially restored. The left hand
of St. Anne is missing.
Literature: Das Schnütgen-Museum, p.84, no.141a; A. Legner, 1970, p.75, no.3
Cologne, Schnütgen-Museum, no.A1051–Donation by Dr. Walther Blancke to the PRO
ARTE MEDII AEVI–Friends of the Schnütgen Museum.

Cologne School,
about 1460/70

49. The Virgin and
Child

The Virgin has a 'Cologne face' as exemplified in the works of Stephan Lochner. The statuette has a delicate balance, the rucked-up draperies of her sumptuous robe enclosing a gently swaying body. Analogous figures can be found in the paintings done in the workshop of the Master of the Life of the Virgin (see nos.13-16). This figure, together with the *'Virgin of the Wide Robe'* (no.50), is a key work and is among the finest small late gothic sculptures made in Cologne. Its style corresponds to that of Cologne panel-painting around 1460/70. It belongs to a group of sculptures which depend stylistically upon the figure of a Virgin in the Church of St. Andreas, Cologne. The latter is an important stylistic document of Cologne sculpture at the time of the Master of the Life of the Virgin.

Walnut, height 35·5cm (1ft 2in), not including the later pedestal; freestanding. The old polychromy, gold robe with blue lining, and carmine red dress, is damaged. The hair is blackened and was originally gilded. Both the Virgin's robe, and her hair at the neck, had been filed down to allow baroque ornaments to be fixed–so, too, the Child's left arm. Small holes at the neck of the figure and the back of the robe were made when a small cloth robe and (still existing) baroque crowns were attached.
Provenance: Possibly from the Cistercian convent at Zissendorf (the statuette being said to have come 'from a nunnery near Siegburg'). The baroque accretions which were formerly attached to the figure also suggest an origin in a convent.
Literature: Das Schnütgen-Museum, no.146; A. Legner, 1970, p.76, no.6; H. P. Hilger, 'Rezension zu A. Legner, Spätgotische Skulpturen im Schnütgen-Museum', *Rheinische Vierteljahrsblätter*, 35, 1971, p.535; A. Legner, *Marienandachtsbilder der Spätgotik: Die Gottesmutter, Marienbild in Rheinland und in Westfalen*, Recklinghausen 1974, p.123.
Cologne, Schnütgen Museum, no.A930.

Lower Rhine
(Cologne?) School,
about 1470/80

50. 'The Virgin of the Wide Robe'

The Virgin is enveloped in a gold robe and stares in front of her; she seems to have a premonition of Christ's Passion and hardly notices the caress of the child. She is the Virgin of Pity, the *Eleusa*. The form of a late gothic statuette and the iconography of a Byzantine icon combine to produce an individual work of devotional art. The colouring is sumptuous, like that of contemporaneous panel paintings. The small size engenders an atmosphere of intimacy and sympathy. A feeling for texture and for gentle sculptural qualities as well as an emphasis on spiritual beauty put this statuette into the tradition of Utrecht madonnas, but even within this context the Cologne sculpture remains strongly individual. If one compares this statuette from the Schnütgen Museum to the oak statue in the Rijksmuseum in Amsterdam attributed to Adriaen van Wesel, one will find close similarities; but it cannot really be upheld that both figures were carved by the same artist. The fact that art historians have attributed the *Virgin of the Wide Robe* variously to a Cologne artist, and also to Adriaen van Wesel (who worked at Utrecht) helps to show how closely linked in style were Utrecht and Cologne, the Netherlands and the Lower Rhine. It is also important to emphasise the stylistic affinity of this sculpture with early works of the Master of St. Bartholomew (nos.30–38), who was familiar with Utrecht art and developed from it.

Walnut, height 39·5cm (1ft 3½in), freestanding. The finish is old, the plinth has additions in plaster and oak.
Literature: Das Schnütgen-Museum, p.84, no.142; H. Meurer, *Das Klever Chorgestühl und Arnt Beeldesnider*, Dusseldorf 1969, p.43,79; A. Legner, 1970, p.25, p.81; Cologne Exhib., 1970, p.103, no.208; H. P. Hilger, 'Rezension zu A. Legner, Spätgotische Skulpturen im Schnütgen-Museum', *Rheinische Vierteljahrsblätter*, 35, 1971, p.536; A. Legner, *Marienandachtsbilder der Spätgotik: Die Gottesmutter, Marienbild im Rheinland und Westfalen*, Recklinghausen 1974, p.123.
Cologne, Schnütgen Museum, no.A783.

Lower Rhine School.
about 1460/70

51. St. Jerome and the
Lion

St. Jerome wears his cardinal's robes with the lion, his attribute, at his feet. The saint bends down towards the lion whose friend he had become. Legend says that a lion came limping to the patriarch for help, showing him his wounded paw. After St. Jerome had removed the thorn, the lion stayed with him as a pet. The saint looks very life-like, with a florid complexion and colourful robes, typical of the naturalism of late gothic wooden sculpture. The figure originally stood among others in the main panel of a late gothic winged altarpiece. Stylistically, the wooden figure belongs to those Cologne workshops which seem to centre on the statue of the Virgin in the Church of St. Andreas. The draperies of the cloak underline the sculptural, voluminous quality of this monumental figure.

Lime, height 153cm (5ft 0¼in), back hollow. Modern plinth, old finish restored; the gilding on the lion is not original. From the church at Lövenich, Erkelenz district.
Literature: Das Schnütgen-Museum, p.92, no.159; A. Legner, 1970, p.77, no.7; H. P. Hilger, 'Rezension zu A. Legner, Spätgotische Skulpturen im Schnütgen-Museum', *Rheinische Vierteljahrsblätter*, 35, 1971, p.536.
Cologne, Schnütgen Museum, no.A201.

Cologne School,
about 1490

52. St. Dorothea

The attribute of the saint is a small basket of apples (see Index of Saints: Dorothea). This is how the Cologne Master of the Holy Kindred (no.20) also shows St. Dorothea. In the painting the figure wears a sumptuous dress, and so did the carved statuette, but the gold brocade has worn less well than in the painting. Stylistically too the statuette is similar to the paintings of the Master of the Holy Kindred and the circle around him. The elaborate polychromatic effect of the pressed brocade, repoussée work, gilding and enamel-like flesh tones suggests how important the work of the painters and gilders of wooden statues was for late gothic sculpture. The statuette, which must date from the end of the 15th century, is also reminiscent of works of Mecheln, Brussels and Antwerp origin. These wooden sculptures are often related so closely that one can even imagine a kind of mass-production. The figure of St. Dorothea, with its excellent and delicately-applied colouring, originated in just such a woodcarving workshop in Cologne towards the end of the 15th century.

Oak, 39cm (1ft 3¼in) high, freestanding. Original polychrome partly reworked. Cologne, Schnütgen Museum, no.A785.

Cologne School,
about 1500/10

53. Female Saint

Among Cologne school paintings, stylistic parallels to this sculpture are mainly found in the panels of the Master of St. Severin (nos.23–28). The figure is closely related to works emanating from the circle around the Cologne sculptor Tilman van der Burch. This artist, and with him the largest Cologne workshop producing late gothic sculpture, was introduced into art history some years ago by Hans Peter Hilger. Among the features which characterise the work of Tilman's workshop at the beginning of the 16th century are a hardening of the draperies; the sharp edges and large creases of the Virgin's draperies belong in this context. It is very probable that Tilman van der Burch is identical with the building foreman of the same name at Cologne Cathedral who is mentioned in 1467. The many sculptures of this group share a strange feature, but one which is symptomatic for the way late gothic woodcarving workshops operated: figures very different from each other in appearance and quality may yet be nearly identical in certain parts and thus show themselves as products of one workshop in spite of their heterogeneous nature. And Tilman presumably employed many carvers of varying degrees of skill who worked according to accepted patterns and made use of models. The composition of this particularly graceful female figure and other closely related statues also shows the influence of a copper engraving by the Master ES. This is quite easily explained, as the carver's pattern-collections contained by this time not only traditional sketches after motifs from Flemish paintings but also more recent models such as woodcuts and engravings by the Master ES, Israhel van Meckenem, Martin Schongauer and Albrecht Dürer, all of which became widely-known around this time.

Said to come from the chapel of Castle Rheineck.

Oak, height 120cm (3ft 11½in), the back hollowed out and boarded up. Remains of original finish. Left hand and attribute of right hand missing, part of robe and piece of hair at the right shoulder broken off.

Literature: H.P.Hilger, 'Der Meister des hl. Christophorus im Dom zu Köln', *Kölner Domblatt*, 26/27, 1967; *Das Schnütgen-Museum*, p.89, no.151; A.Legner, 1970, p.84; H.P Hilger, 'Zum Werk des Kölner Bildhauers Tilman van der Burch', *Zeitschrift des Deutschen Vereins für Kunstwissenschaft*, 23, 1969, p.61; H.P.Hilger, 'Eine spätgotische Mantelschliesse im Münsterschatz zu Essen', *Pantheon*, 29, 1971, p.323; H.P.Hilger, 'Ein Altarschrein des Kölner Bildhauers Tilman van der Burch in Breitscheid', *Festschrift für Franz Graf Wolff Metternich*, 1974, p.142; H.Krohm, *Die spätgotische Muttergottes im Kloster Neuwerk und verwandte Kölner Kunstwerke: Die Abtei Gladbach 974–1802*, Mönchengladbach 1974, p.133.

Cologne, Schnütgen Museum, no.A829.

54. Angels carrying
Scrolls
See colour plate facing p.155

The decorative style of these two angels (particularly noticeable in the borders of their copes) can be best compared with the paintings of the Cologne artist Bartholomäus Bruyn. On the scrolls are quotations from the Bible: Proverbs, XXVIII,13: ('*He who conceals his transgressions will not prosper, but he who confesses and forsakes them will obtain mercy*'); St. Luke, XV,7: ('*Just so, I tell you, there will be more joy in heaven over one sinner who repents than over ninety-nine righteous persons who need no repentance*'); St. Matthew, III,2: ('*Repent, for the kingdom of heaven is at hand*'). These quotations relate to the remission of sins and show these two angels to be connected with the practice of confession and penance. Large figures of angels with scrolls and the instruments of martyrdom had an important iconographical place on the outside of confessionals (which had only come into general use after the Tridentinum). The splendid and ornate liturgical robes, curled hair and colourful wings (only partly original) of these angels create a festive, solemn impression. The figures' stance is a balanced counterpoint, their stature is imposing; they are sumptuous, brightly-coloured and decorative – products of the German Renaissance with late gothic origins.

Fruitwood, height 127 and 120cm (4ft 2in × 3ft 11½in), backs flattened. The robe-clasps are lost, the old finish has been restored.
Literature: Das Schnütgen-Museum, p.94, no.160; A. Legner, 1970, p.100; H. P. Hilger, 'Rezension zu A. Legner, Spätgotische Skulpturen im Schnütgen-Museum', *Rheinische Vierteljahrsblätter*, 35, 1971, p.536.
Cologne, Schnütgen Museum, no.A860a,b.

56. Cushion-Cover
showing a Young
Woman with a Unicorn

In the centre of the cushion-cover is a wreath of thistles; from it a dense network of sharply-pointed thistle-leaves and flowers spreads out to the edges.

The scene is set in the centre of this wreath. The girl wears a red dress with a pleated front and a fashionable head-dress; flowers suggest that she is sitting in a meadow. She guards herself with her left hand against the unicorn which approaches from the right. It has its forefeet in her lap, its head raised. Tall flowers (carnations, roses and lily of the valley) fill the background.

The virgin and the unicorn have always been a favourite theme in the visual arts as well as in literature. In many cases it is not clear whether the scene is to be interpreted as a symbol of secular love, as a visual representation of chastity (legend says that the wild unicorn can only be caught and tamed by a virgin) or as a religious theme.

Stephan Lochner painted the scene twice, both times in the form of an ornament on the clasp of the Virgin's robe; this suggests how the scene on the cushion-cover should be interpreted. The 'crown of thorns', which encircles the virgin and unicorn, alludes to Christ. The *Physiologus*, the late classical treatise on nature and its allegorical significance, which remained influential throughout the Middle Ages, sees in the unicorn a symbol for Christ who 'flees into the lap of the Virgin' (Behling). Other details also refer to Christ, e.g. the scented plants, particularly the carnation, which acts as a symbol of Christ's Passion (Behling). These leave no doubt that the scene has a religious significance.

Betty Kurth has brought together a whole group of cushion-covers showing the virgin and unicorn set in a wreath; they were all done in Lower Germany in the 15th century and prove that the theme was frequently used and much liked.

Tapestry-woven panel, embroidered with silk and gold threads. About 60 × 60cm (1ft 11½in square).
Literature: B. Kurth, *Die deutschen Bildteppiche des Mittelalters*, Vienna 1926, p.196; Catalogue: *Bildteppiche aus sechs Jahrhunderten*, Hamburg 1953, no.32; L. Behling, *Die Pflanzenwelt der mittelalterlichen Kathedralen*, Cologne/Graz 1964, p.109; Das Schnütgen-Museum, no.141; Cologne Exhib., 1970, no.453; J. W. Einhorn, *Spiritalis Unicornis. Das Einhorn als Bedeutungstrager in Literatur und Kunst des Mittelalters*, Munich 1976, no.206E. Cologne, Schnütgen Museum, no. P210.

57. Border showing the Coronation of the Virgin

This colourful border with a gold ground was used as the trimming of an altar-frontal and shows the *Coronation of the Virgin*, flanked on both sides by three pairs of apostles. Each pair stands in front of an architectural frame with backgrounds of different fabrics. This frame serves at the same time as a pedestal for musical angels. Such angels are often incorporated into this scene as they add splendour to the event of the coronation of the Queen of Heaven. The coronation itself (in the centre) is emphasised by a more elaborate architectural frame. The Virgin, already crowned, sits to the left; she wears a red dress ornamented with gold threads and a blue robe with a yellow facing. Christ is enthroned beside her. In his left hand he holds the globe, his right hand is raised in benediction. He too wears a splendid gown of red velvet and various gold patterns. The garments are shown in strong relief. On either side are two angels swinging a censer, and two playing a portative organ and a trumpet.

The apostles face each other. They are shown in three-quarter profile and carry their attributes. Their robes are hardly less splendid than those of the Virgin and Christ. To the extreme left are the apostles Peter and Andrew; then come Saints John the Evangelist and Paul; then James the Less and Judas Thaddeus. To the right of the coronation are Simon and James the Great; then Bartholomew and Philip; and finally Thomas and Matthew.

The angels around them play a large variety of instruments, such as a lute, zither, triangle, tambourine, cymbals and bombard. This angelic orchestra demonstrates the diversity of mediaeval musical instruments.

The border is dated 1500 at the right-hand edge; this is unusual. The style, however, corresponds to this date. The colourful and sumptuous clothes are typical of the period; for instance, they are also found in the work of the Master of the St. Bartholomew Altarpiece and of the Master of St. Severin, whose figures in the *Adoration of the Magi* (see no.25) have similar faces.

This border takes pride of place among similar textiles produced in Cologne, an industry which flourished towards the end of the 15th century.

Embroidered altar-border. On a woven ground the appliquéd figures of the apostles, the Virgin and Christ are embroidered in silk and metallic threads. The angels are embroidered directly on to the ground in silk and metallic threads. About 16 × 205cm (6¼in × 6ft 8¾in). Up to 1920 at St. Alban, Cologne.
Literature: E. Schreyer, *Die Kölner Bortenweberei des Mittelalters*, Augsburg (1932), no.50; R. Jaques, *Deutsche Textilkunst*, Berlin (1942), p.179.
Cologne, Schnütgen Museum, no. P156.

Cologne School,
about 1420

58. Christ Carrying
the Cross
and The Crucifixion

(a) *Christ Carrying the Cross.* The group of Christ and three soldiers is set in an architectural frame; the illusion of depth is created by a floor which juts out like a plinth, and an obliquely set canopy with two ogee arches.

Christ is shown bowed down under the weight of the cross. He walks towards the left, turning his head with its crown of thorns away from the soldiers. The soldiers surround him and mock him. Christ's face is marked by a quiet sadness, the coarser faces of the soldiers no more than hint at their brutality.

(b) *Crucifixion.* The scene is set in an architectural frame which, unlike the frame in *Christ Carrying the Cross,* consists of three *round* arches, the central one ending in corbels. The Virgin and St. John stand beside the cross. The richly-folded, softly-flowing draperies aptly express the statuesque effect of the figures. The Virgin holds a handkerchief to her eyes and St. John has folded his hands in front of his chest. The fragile-looking body of the dead Christ is draped with a loin-cloth.

The two panels can be related to a group of Cologne stained-glass paintings which show close stylistic similarities. The Schnütgen Museum possesses a stained-glass painting of the *Pietà* (M 525) which has a very similar framing system. It is likely that they originated in the same workshop. This also applies to the (later) window of the *Trinity* in the north transept of Cologne Cathedral (which in turn goes back to the west window of the Cistercian abbey of Altenberg near Cologne). Other closely-related panels were at Castle Gondorf on the Moselle (now Ludwig Collection, Aachen) and in Berlin (Palace Museum, destroyed).

Among the panel paintings of the Cologne school there are connections with the work of the Master of St. Veronica (see nos.6 and 7). In the '*Small Calvary*' for instance, the faces of the holy women and St. John (and also the atmosphere of muted sadness) are reminiscent of the stained-glass paintings. The figure of Christ in *Christ Carrying the Cross* (Kisters Collection, Kreuzlingen) by the same master also shows distinct similarities to the glass painting of *Christ Carrying the Cross,* particularly in the pose and facial expression.

Stained glass, 137 × 58·5cm (4ft 6in × 1ft 11in) each.
Restored: (a) *Christ Carrying the Cross.* Pane showing left-hand side of plinth; pane showing left foot of soldier on the left; pane showing left-hand gablet.
(b) *Crucifixion.* Pane showing right-hand side of canopy; parts of panes above the upper iron cross-bar.
Chapel of the Starkenberg house, 10 Heumarkt, Cologne, which was demolished in 1907.
Literature: Das Schnütgen Museum, no.123 (*Christ Carrying the Cross* only); Catalogue: *Rhein und Maas,* Cologne 1972, Q17, Q18; Cologne Exhib., 1974, nos.64,65; H. Rode, 'Die mittelalterlichen Glasmalereien des Kölner Domes', *CVMA Deutschland,* IV, I, 'Köln, Dom', Berlin 1974, p.173
Cologne, Schnütgen Museum, no. M 167 a/b

59. The Virgin and
Child with St. Ursula

The Virgin and St. Ursula are shown standing in an interior. The Virgin wears a crown, a brocade dress and a robe with long, diagonal folds. St. Ursula, standing beside her, holds a book in her left hand and, in her right hand, two arrows whose points have been damaged (see Index of Saints: Ursula). She wears a light-blue dress and a robe which is held together at the neck by a brooch and gathered up at the waist; its folds are sharp-edged. Both women look at the naked Christ Child sitting on the Virgin's right arm and abstractedly reaching for a fruit which the Virgin offers him with a gracious gesture.

Similarly energetically-modelled faces and tautly-drawn draperies are to be found in the Merode panes (so called after the family of their donors) in the Hessisches Landesmuseum, Darmstadt (no.Kg 33: 2a, 2b, 2c); the fragment of a head of St. George in the Schnütgen Museum (no.M634) also shows similarities.

The style of the St. Ursula panel is further developed in the large cycle of the *Life of Christ* which is now in the Chapel of the Holy Sacrament at Cologne cathedral, but which presumably originated in the cloisters of St. Cecilia. The style of the St. Ursula panel is still distinctly reminiscent of Stephan Lochner's art, but the harder draperies and sharper faces already progress beyond it.

Stained glass, 75 × 49cm (2ft 5½in × 1ft 7¼in).
Restored: Pane showing part of the Virgin's robe; various panes showing parts of the background; pane showing upper part of the architectural frame.
Literature: Das Schnütgen Museum, no.141b; H. Rode, op.cit., pp.155,173.
Cologne, Schnütgen Museum, no. M521.

The Vision of Saint Bernard, by the Master of the Life of the Virgin (cat.no.14)

Saints Roch and Nicasius with Nicasius Hackenay, by the Master of the Holy Kindred (Cat. no.19)

Angel with a Scroll, by
an anonymous
master of the
Cologne school,
about 1530
(Cat. no.54)

Index of Saints

There are included only these saints who have a particular significance for Cologne or who play an important part in the objects on display.

Saint Achatius

The legend of Achatius and his 10,000 companions was unknown before the late 14th century. The saint was said to be the leader of a group of Roman soldiers on campaign in Syria. They were converted through the appearance of an angel, and were eventually martyred by crucifixion on Mount Ararat. Before death, the martyrs were tortured with sharp stakes. Consequently, Achatius and his followers are normally shown holding short boughs whittled to a point.

See no.19

Saint Agnes

Accounts of her life vary considerably, but all agree that she was martyred at the age of twelve, perhaps around the year 251. Some say that she refused marriage to the Prefect of Rome's son (her name derives from the Greek meaning 'chaste'). The *Golden Legend* tells that, because of her refusal to marry, she was paraded through the streets naked (but escaped shame because of her long hair) before being committed to a brothel. A prospective client was miraculously struck dead. Martyrdom soon followed.

Agnes is invariably shown accompanied by a lamb. This would appear to be an attribute accorded her for no more reason than the coincidental resemblance of her name to the Latin *agnus* (=lamb).

See no.37

Saint Alexius

His legend relates that he was the son of a Roman senator. He abandoned his wife on their wedding night and travelled abroad dressed as a poor pilgrim. He is said to have lived as a beggar–17 years in Edessa (Greece), and 17 years under a staircase in his father's house. He left behind him a posthumous statement of his faith, and an explanation of his conduct.

See nos.26,37

Saint Anne

The mother of the Virgin. A 6th-century text tells of how she conceived miraculously and gave birth to the Virgin Mary (see also *Holy Kindred*).

She is most commonly shown (as in no.48) with the Virgin and Child, a composition which displays the three generations of the Church. The composition gradually became more and more naturalistic, but no.48 shows a fairly typical example of the Gothic arrangement, displaying a hierarchy of size.

See nos.19,48

Saint Apollonia
Saint Apollonia led an active Christian life in Alexandria in the 3rd century. She was tortured by having her teeth drawn by pincers; then, when threatened with death by burning, she gladly accepted martyrdom by throwing herself on the fire. She is normally shown holding pincers, and is known as a protectress against toothache and as the patroness of dentists.

See nos.26,55

Saint Augustine
Bishop of Hippo in North Africa, born in 354, died 430. He is revered as one of the Fathers of the Church. 'One of the most prolific geniuses that humanity has ever known', his *Confessions* tell the story of his conversion after a dissolute youth. His attribute is a heart, which symbolises his fervent spirit.

See nos.12,16

Saint Barbara
Said to have lived in Syria in the 3rd century, Saint Barbara's story was not formulated until the 7th century. She was locked up in a tower by her father, in order to exclude suitors. Nevertheless, she persuaded some builders to create an additional window bringing the number to three. A priest entered by means of the extra window and baptised her, whereupon she described her windows as symbols of Father, Son and Holy Ghost. Her conduct angered her father, who eventually beheaded her and was himself struck dead by lightning in recompense. She is protectress against lightning and sudden death in general; she appears frequently in association with warrior saints.

See nos.19,20,26

Saint Benedict
Born around 480, died around 543. The founder of the oldest monastic order in Western Europe, which is named from him and which places emphasis on manual labour as well as spiritual discipline. He may be shown wearing the black habit of the Benedictine Order, but sometimes wears the white robe of the later (reformed) groups.

See no.16

Saint Bernard
Saint Bernard of Clairvaux (1090–1153). He founded the monastery of Clairvaux in 1115 and passed there a life famous for its energy in the study of theology and in the championing of the Cistercian order. 'He is the founder of the mysticism of the Middle Ages' (Holweck).

The scene from his life which is most often dipicted is that of his vision of the Virgin and Child (see no.14). Legend says that, when he was writing his famous praise of the Virgin (the '*Homilies on the Song of Solomon*'), she appeared to him and wet his lips from the milk of her breast, thereby endowing him (some say) with supernatural eloquence.

See nos.14,16

Saint Brigid	Saint Brigid of Kildare, a patroness of Ireland, was born about 451, became abbess about 468 and died in 521. She is principally famous for erecting her convent of Kil-dara ('church of the oak'), which became the chief one in Ireland. She was celebrated in many German dioceses including Cologne. See no.26
Saint Bruno	Born in Cologne about 1030, he was ordained there and became canon of the church of Saint Kunibert. He retired, with companions, to the wilderness near Grenoble and founded the Carthusian Order (named after the mountain range, 'La Chartreuse'). See no.20
Saint Catherine of Alexandria	Saint Catherine has now been removed from the Catholic Calendar because of her doubtful authenticity. In the 15th century she was highly popular and much painted. The *Golden Legend* tells that she was a Queen. Greatly erudite, she outdid in argument fifty Greek philosophers. They were put to death, for their failure, by the Emperor Maxentius. He attempted to put Catherine to death on a spiked wheel, which was however split asunder, leaving Catherine unharmed. She was later killed by decapitation, her body being borne away by angels to Mount Sinai. See nos.11,19,26
Saint Cecilia	Saint Cecilia is thought to have been active in the 3rd century in Rome. She was betrothed to Valerianus, even though she had taken a vow of chastity. 'While being led to her betrothed's house on her wedding day to the sound of musical instruments, she invoked only God in her heart, asking him the favour of keeping her soul and body without stain.' She asked her husband that they should lead a virginal life. He agreed, on condition that he be allowed to see his bride's protecting angel; the angel descended to place garlands of roses and lilies on their heads (see no.37). Both were later martyred. From the mention of music at her wedding, Cecilia became the patroness of musicians. See nos.26,37
Saint Christopher	Now removed from the Catholic Church Calendar because of doubts about his authenticity. The *Golden Legend* describes him as a giant who worked as a ferryman on a river. He was induced to carry across the river a small child who grew heavier and heavier. The infant revealed himself as Christ and explained that his great weight was attributable to the world, which he carried on his shoulders. He ordered Christopher to plant his staff, which accordingly sprang to life and bore fruit. Christopher is known as the patron of travellers. See no.18

Saint Cordula   Cordula's relics were found in 1278; some of them were preserved in the church of Saints John and Cordula, Cologne. Her legend appends an episode to the story of Saint Ursula. She was one of the 11,000 virgins, but was too faint-hearted to accept martyrdom with the others. Accordingly, she lay still to avoid detection as her companions died around her. On the day after the massacre, she repented of her cowardice, showed herself, and consequently shared the martyrdom of the others. She is very rarely shown in art objects. No.11 shows what may be one of her few appearances.

Saint Dionysius   Saint Dionysius (or Denis) was bishop of Paris in the 3rd century. After martyrdom through decapitation, he is said to have carried his own head either *to* or *from* Montmartre (the Mount of Martyrs). He is patron against headache.

See no.55

Saint Dorothea   Dorothea (or Dorothy) is said to have been martyred in Cappadocia, Asia Minor. The part of her legend most frequently referred to is related in the *Golden Legend*.

Dorothea was sentenced to death when she refused to give up her Christian beliefs. On the way to her execution an unbelieving scribe (Theophilus) challenged her to send him some roses and apples from the heavenly garden which she declared she was soon to enter. After her martyrdom, a young child delivered a basket of roses and apples to Theophilus, thus effecting his conversion.

See nos.20,30,52

Saint Elizabeth   Saint Elizabeth of Hungary (or of Thuringia), has always been venerated in the German-speaking regions. Her relics were enshrined at Marburg. 'She attained the highest degree of Christian perfection' (Holweck). Active in the 13th century, she lived in voluntary poverty performing multitudinous works of charity, 'for her love of the poor was boundless'. Thus, she is most often shown in pictures carrying bread for the poor, and with a beggar appealing to her. She is crowned, since she was the daughter of Andreas II of Hungary, and wears the habit of a Franciscan nun.

See no.19

Saint Genovefa   Saint Genovefa (Geneviève) is the patron saint of Paris. Born about 422, she is said to have played an important role in the defence of Paris against the Huns and Franks. Her attributes include a candle (referring to an episode in her legend which resembles closely that of Saint Gudula). In no.19 a devil extinguishes the candle with a pair of bellows, only for it to be relit by an angel.

Saint Gereon

Gereon is Cologne's warrior saint. His legend was formulated in the 13th century and takes the form of a sub-plot to the story of Saint Maurice and the Theban Legion. Maurice, the Commander of Roman troops from Thebes in Egypt, refused to carry out certain pagan rites. He and his legion were consequently massacred. Gereon and *his* group of 318 Thebans and 360 Mauretanians were similarly martyred near Cologne.

Some bones, now venerated as Gereon's, were found in the 12th century, some 800 years after the putative date of the Massacre. They rest in the church of Saint Gereon in Cologne.

See nos.16,18

Saint Gertrude

The saint who appears in no.26 is Gertrude of Nivelles, who was much celebrated in the late Middle Ages. Born in 631, she was elected abbess of Nivelles (Belgium) in 652. Known for her knowledge of the scriptures, she is venerated as protectress against rats, mice and fever, and also as a patron of travellers.

Saint Gregory

Gregory I (the Great) was Pope from 590 to his death in 604. He distinguished himself by giving a set form to parts of the mass and to some ecclesiastical chants. It was his work on the mass which perhaps inspired representations of the *Mass of Saint Gregory*. It is said that on one occasion during divine service he prayed God for a sign in order to convince an unbeliever of the truth. Above the altar there appeared Christ as the Man of Sorrows surrounded by the Instruments of the Passion.

See no.16

Saint Gudula

Educated by her godmother, Saint Gertrude of Nivelles (q.v.). After Gertrude's death (in 659) she retired to her father's house and led a pious life until her death in 712. Her relics have, since the 11th century, been in the church of Ste. Gudule in Brussels, the town of which she is patroness.

Saint Gudula is said to have been in the habit of making a long walk through the night in order to arrive at church in time for morning prayer. On one occasion the devil extinguished her lantern, which relit itself in answer to the Saint's prayers. She is, therefore, shown with a lantern.

See no.19

Saint Helena

Born around 255, she was the daughter of Constantine the Great. Her main achievement was the foundation of churches in the Holy Land. While there she found the buried Cross of Christ, which she had earlier seen in a vision.

See nos.19,26

Holy Kindred

The Holy Kindred (as seen in no.19) is a subject most popular during the 15th century, and seen most frequently in Cologne.

It is related to the theme of the Virgin and Child with Saint Anne. The legend tells that Saint Anne (q.v.), the Virgin's mother, was married three times, and each time produced a daughter named Mary. Each daughter married and had children. This is probably most easily expressed by the diagram.

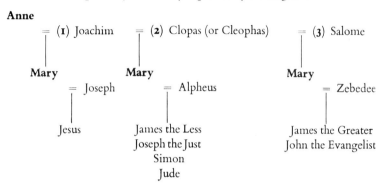

Anne

= (**1**) Joachim   = (**2**) Clopas (or Cleophas)   = (**3**) Salome

Mary   **Mary**   **Mary**
   = Joseph   = Alpheus   = Zebedee

   Jesus   James the Less   James the Greater
                       Joseph the Just   John the Evangelist
                       Simon
                       Jude

Saint Hubert

Saint Hubert was the first bishop of Liège from 722 to 727. His legend was not formulated until late and certain episodes are 'absolutely mythical' (Holweck). One of them, the meeting with the stag, is said to have been borrowed from the apocryphal acts of Saint Eustace. As shown in no.16a, Hubert was, as a young man, a devotee of hunting, among other worldly pleasures. When hunting on Good Friday he was confronted by a stag with a vision of the cross mounted between its antlers. Hubert was converted by this miracle.

A later and rarely-depicted part of the legend is seen in no.16c. It is said that when Hubert was being invested as a bishop, an angel appeared with his stole. He is already celebrating mass when the angel appears.

Hubert is, traditionally, the patron saint of hunters, but his popularity in late 15th-century Cologne may be connected with the importance of the Schwarz-Hirtz family. The name is very like the words meaning *black stag* (Schwarz' Hirsch), a beast which forms part of the family coat-of-arms. This may explain the unusual dark colour of the stag in no.16a. (Usually, the stag is white.) The suggestion that the Werden altar may have been commissioned by the family may be supported by the depiction in no.16d of another saint accompanied by a deer – Saint Giles.

Saint Jerome

A native of Dalmatia, he is one of the four Fathers of the Church. Born around 341, died 420. He is revered as a promulgator of the monastic way of life, and is often shown working in his study. Usually dressed as a cardinal, he is invariably accompanied by a lion. Legend tells that he withdrew a thorn from the paw of a lion, which thereupon became devoted to him. Cologne artists frequently adopt the same formula, representing the lion as reaching up to the saint, rather like a domestic cat.

See nos.11,37,51

Saint Lawrence

Saint Lawrence (or Laurentuis) was martyred in the year 258. Of Spanish birth, he became archdeacon of Rome. When the clergy were being persecuted by Valerian, Lawrence distributed the wealth of the church to the poor.

The Prefect, ignorant of this generosity, incarcerated Saint Lawrence, who promised to tell the whereabouts of the church treasures after three days. He brought the poor of the city to the Prefect, and indicated *them* as the church treasures. Saint Lawrence was then martyred by means of roasting on a gridiron. He is the patron saint of the poor.

See no.22

Saint Leodegar

Born about 616, he became bishop of Autun in 659. Falling foul of Thierry III, he was tortured and martyred. He is often shown holding a boring-tool which was said to have been used to blind him.

See no.19

Saint Ludger

Ordained priest at Cologne in 777, he joined the Benedictine order when in Italy some years later. In 804 he was consecrated bishop of Münster and founded the abbey at Werden, where he was buried.

See no.16

Saint Maurice

Saint Maurice's legend was composed in the 5th century, although he is said to have been martyred about 303. The authenticity of the legend is much disputed. He was the commander of a legion of soldiers, all of whom were Christians. When he and his men refused to give thanksgiving for military victory to pagan gods, they were massacred by their fellow-soldiers. The place of massacre was in Switzerland, where a town takes its name from the saint. He is usually depicted as a dark-skinned (Moorish?) soldier, wearing a red cross on his breastplate.

See nos.16,17

Saint Nicasius

An obscure saint rarely shown in works of art. He was bishop of Reims in 400, and was responsible for building the church of Notre Dame there (now the Cathedral). Killed in the church in 407 by the Vandals.

See no.19

Saint Roch

Saint Roch (Rochus or Rock) was renowned as a protector against infection, and therefore appears frequently as an intercessor for donors. His exploits may be no more than legend. He came from Montpellier (France) and was active in the 14th century, travelling much. He is thought to have suffered from the plague, but was saved when a dog led its master to the place where the saint lay afflicted. After his recovery he returned to Montpellier, but, unrecognised because of the ravages of disease, was thrown into prison and died there. He is generally shown with a sore on his leg. Often he is accompanied by an angel, or the dog, and is characterised as a pilgrim (since he made the journey to Rome).

See no.19

Three Magi	The Three Magi (or Three Kings, or Wise Men) played a most important part in the history of Cologne, although they never, of course, visited the city. The fullest version of their story is given by Johannes von Hildesheim, his text first published in the 16th century but known earlier.

The Three Magi (or Three Kings, or Wise Men) played a most important part in the history of Cologne, although they never, of course, visited the city. The fullest version of their story is given by Johannes von Hildesheim, his text first published in the 16th century but known earlier.

Mentioned briefly in the New Testament, the Magi had by the late Middle Ages, become definite types – the oldest being called Caspar, the negro Balthazar and the youngest Melchior. Since they were said to be Kings, their adoration of the Infant Christ demonstrated the submission of temporal powers to the authority of the Church. Their gifts were thought to reflect various facets of Christ's character and biography – gold was given in homage to the Child's Kingship; frankincense was proper to his divinity; myrrh (used for embalming) prefigured his physical death, and his triumph over it.

The bones of the Magi were given by the Emperor Frederick Barbarossa to Rainald von Dassel, archbishop of Cologne, who brought them from Milan to Cologne in 1164. They still rest in the shrine begun for them in 1181 by Nicholas of Verdun. The political importance of the shrine cannot be overestimated. Since the original Three Kings were the first to be blessed by Christ, they came to be thought of as the first *Christian* Kings, their kingship having been 'confirmed' by Christ. In accordance with this belief, the German emperors, after coronation in nearby Aachen, came to Cologne to receive confirmation at the shrine of the Magi.

The cathedral of Cologne was originally named as the 'Church of Saint Peter and the Holy Three Kings' (Saint Peter's chain and crozier were also preserved there); the town coat-of-arms displayed (and still does display) the three crowns of the Magi. The intrinsic power of the Kings and their shrine took on a great popular appeal, partly due to the fact that the Kings came to be venerated as the patron saints of all pilgrims and travellers. People voyaging up the Rhine felt impelled to break their journey and make contact with the first Christian pilgrims.

These circumstances explain the proliferation of images of the Magi in Cologne. It is small wonder that the most important commission to be given by the town council in the 15th century was for a large *Adoration of the Magi*, which hung in the Ratshaus itself. The *Adoration* places worldly wealth, inherited power and over-dressed privilege in relation to the (literally) naked spiritual truth represented by Christ – its relevance to Cologne, where many citizens could identify with the wealthy Magi, is clear.

See nos.2,3,24,25,32

Saint Ursula	Ursula and 11,000 British virgins are said to have been martyred in Cologne on 21st October in the year 237. The perpetrators of this massacre were thought to be Huns returning from defeat at Chalons in 451 – 'the anachronism', as Baring-Gould says, 'is considerable'.

Ursula and 11,000 British virgins are said to have been martyred in Cologne on 21st October in the year 237. The perpetrators of this massacre were thought to be Huns returning from defeat at Chalons in 451 – 'the anachronism', as Baring-Gould says, 'is considerable'.

The legend has very little historical foundation and seems to have been first formulated in the 10th century, at which time the phrase *XI MM VV* (i.e. eleven virgins martyrs) was mis-interpreted as XI *Millia Virginium* (i.e. 11,000 virgins).

The narrative is as follows: Ursula was the daughter of King Deonotus of Britain (he too is fictive). Her hand was sought by a pagan prince. Ursula claimed a three-year respite during which time she preserved her chastity by sailing the seas accompanied by 11,000 virgins in a convoy of 11 ships. A storm drove the ships up the Rhine to Basle, where the maids disembarked and walked to Rome in order to visit the holy sites. On their return journey they found Cologne to be besieged by the pagan Huns, who immediately massacred the virgins. Ursula was spared because of her beauty, but on refusing to marry the leader of the Huns, was shot with three arrows, and thus martyred.

In the 12th century, a site in Cologne was excavated and found to contain the remains of a large number of people. These were immediately venerated as the relics of Ursula's chaste company. Some difficulty arose when the bones of children and men were uncovered. Piety prevailed, however, when a contemporary mystic, Saint Elizabeth of Schönau, was favoured with a vision of the massacre, and revealed that the virgins were accompanied by Pope Cyriacus and a number of dukes, bishops, and even Ursula's betrothed, all of whom had been attracted by the piety of Ursula's company and had followed it to the end.

Ursula is primarily revered in Cologne, where several cycles of paintings decorate churches (see no.21). Thomas Coryate, who wrote the first real English travel book in 1611, described the display of relics in the Church of Saint Ursula – 'On three sides, their bones lie in great heaps together; under them are placed their skulls.'

Baring-Gould points out that the character of Saint Ursula is derived from the Swabian (pagan) goddess Hörsel.

See nos.21,26

Saint Veronica

Veronica is the name given to a woman whose lineage is given differently in the various versions of her legend. All agree on one thing – that the woman wiped Christ's face with a cloth as he was on the road to Calvary, and that the cloth (the sudarium) became imprinted with the image of Christ's face. The supposed cloth is preserved as a holy relic in Saint Peter's, Rome.

Veronica's name is said to be derived from the phrase 'vera icon' (i.e. 'true image'), which describes the face of Christ on the sudarium. This face is variously shown in paintings. Sometimes Christ is youthful and unblemished, more often he wears the crown of thorns and bears signs of suffering.

Veronica is the patron saint of laundrywomen.

See no.6

S. Baring-Gould, *Curious Myths of the Middle Ages*, 1868.
The Rt. Rev. F. G. Holweck, *A Biographical Dictionary of the Saints*, London, 1924.
The Golden Legend of Jacobus de Voragine, trans. by G. Ryan and H. Ripperberger, 2 vols, London, 1941.